PHYSICS 11

NELSON

UNIV

STUDY GUIDE

SENIOR PROGRAM CONSULTANT

Maurice DiGiuseppe, Ph.D.
University of Ontario Institute of Technology (UOIT)
Formerly of Toronto Catholic District School Board

NELSON / EDUCATION

NELSON EDUCATION

Nelson Physics 11 Study Guide

Senior Program Consultant
Maurice DiGiuseppe

Student Book Authors
Maurice DiGiuseppe
Christopher T. Howes
Jacob Speijer
Charles Stewart
Henri M. van Bemmel
Rob Vucic
Victoria Wraight

Editorial Director
Linda Allison

Acting Publisher, Science
David Spiegel

Managing Editor, Development
Jennifer Hounsell

Product Manager
Lorraine Lue

Program Manager
Carmen Yu

Developmental Editors
Betty Robinson
Sarah Tanzini

Editorial Assistant
Michelle Irvine

Copyeditor
Linda Szostak

Design Director
Ken Phipps

Interior Design
Courtney Hellam

Cover Design
Eugene Lo
Ken Phipps

Cover Image
Jean-Francois Podevin/
Science Photo Library

Asset Coordinator
Suzanne Peden

Illustrators
Crowle Art Group
Stephen Hall
Stephen Hutching
Samuel Laterza
Dave McKay
Allan Moon
Suzanne Peden
PreMediaGlobal
Nicolle Rager Fuller
Theresa Sakno
Ann Sanderson
Ralph Voltz

Compositor
PreMediaGlobal

Cover Research
Debbie Yea

Printer
Transcontinental Printing, Ltd.

Reviewers
The authors and publisher gratefully acknowledge the contributions of the following educators:
Charles J. Cohen
Mark Kinoshita
Richard LaChapelle
Anne Patrick
Steve Pfisterer

Contents

Unit 4 Waves and Sound 125

Unit 5 Electricity and Magnetism 177

Chapter 1: Motion in a Straight Line

Kinematics is the mathematical description of motion. Motion in one direction can be described using scalar and vector quantities. Scalars are quantities with magnitude only, such as distance and speed. Vector quantities, such as displacement and velocity, include direction in addition to magnitude. Multiple vectors can be added graphically by connecting them tip to tail, or they can be added algebraically.

Average speed is the total distance travelled divided by the time taken to travel the distance. Velocity is the rate of change of displacement, or change in position over time. Acceleration is the rate of change in velocity. Motion with constant velocity (zero acceleration) is motion in a straight line at a constant speed.

Graphs of displacement, velocity, and acceleration show mathematical relationships between these quantities. The slope of the tangent line on a displacement–time graph is equal to the object's velocity. The slope of a velocity–time graph is equal to the object's acceleration. The area between the velocity curve and the time axis equals the object's displacement. Similarly, the area under the acceleration curve equals the change in velocity. It is thus possible to use the graph of one characteristic of motion (displacement, velocity, or acceleration) to construct graphs of other characteristics.

Five key equations are useful in solving problems involving uniform acceleration. For such problems, consider which variables are known and which variable is desired. Then select the equation that best fits the known and desired quantities.

Gravity near Earth's surface causes all unsupported objects to fall with a uniform acceleration of approximately 9.8 m/s^2. When air resistance is equal to the force due to gravity acting on a falling object, the object eventually reaches a constant velocity called terminal velocity.

Chapter 2: Motion in Two Dimensions

Vectors can point in any given direction within a plane. For motion in two dimensions, vectors are added graphically by drawing them using a convenient scale and their respective directions, and then placing them tip to tail.

Algebraic vector addition is more accurate than scale vector drawings, especially when more than two vectors are involved. The vectors are broken into their x-components and y-components. These components are then added in their respective dimensions, and the sums are combined using the Pythagorean theorem to give the magnitude of the resultant vector. The tangent function provides the direction of the resultant vector.

Projectile motion, or motion in two independent dimensions, can be analyzed using the five key equations of motion. The horizontal acceleration is zero and the vertical acceleration is that due to gravity. Both motions are subject to the same time of flight.

BIG IDEAS

- Motion involves a change in the position of an object over time.
- Motion can be described using mathematical relationships.
- Many technologies that apply concepts related to kinematics have societal and environmental implications.

Distance, Position, and Displacement

Textbook pp. 8–13

Vocabulary

kinematics	distance (d)	scalar	position ($\vec{d}$)	vector scale diagram
motion	direction	vector	displacement ($\Delta\vec{d}$)	directed line segment

MAIN IDEA: Motion can be described in terms of distance, position, and displacement.

1. Complete **Table 1**. K/U

   Table 1 Kinematics Definitions

Definition	Term
where an object is located	
how far an object has travelled	
how much an object's position has changed	

2. You walk to the corner store after school to buy a carton of milk before going home. The store is 750 m south of the school, and your house is 625 m north of the school. T/I

   (a) What distance have you travelled since leaving the school?

   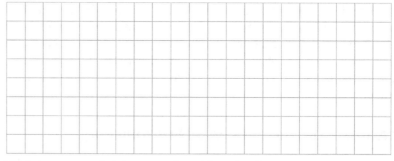

   (b) What is your net displacement from the school?

3. Now suppose the store in Question 2 is the reference point for position. Comment on whether the distance or the displacement depends on the point taken as the zero position. K/U T/I

MAIN IDEA: A scalar is a quantity that has magnitude (size) only, and a vector is a quantity that has magnitude and direction.

4. Complete **Table 2** by identifying whether the quantities are vectors or scalars. K/U

Table 2 Describing Quantities: Scalar or Vector

Quantity	Scalar or vector
where you live relative to your best friend's house	
the temperature in this room	
600 km [S]	
the number of apples in an orchard	
5.23 cm	

MAIN IDEA: You can determine total displacement by using a vector scale diagram.

5. An airplane flies 540 km [E] out of an airport before making an emergency landing at another airport 260 km [W] from its present location. Use a scaled vector diagram to determine the total displacement of the airplane. K/U

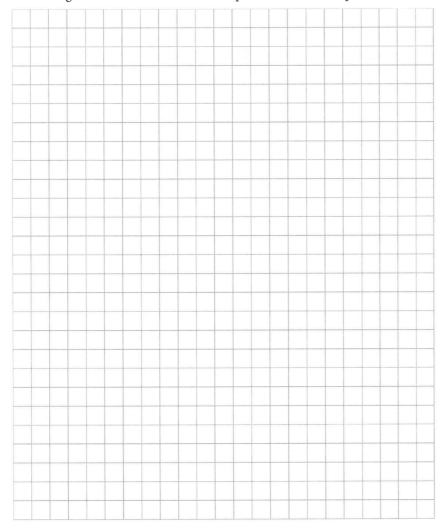

1.2 Speed and Velocity

Textbook pp. 14–20

Vocabulary

average speed (v_{av})	position–time graph	rise	motion with uniform or constant velocity
average velocity ($\vec{v}_{av}$)	slope (m)	run	motion with non-uniform velocity (accelerated motion)

LEARNING TIP

Rounding in Calculations
As a general rule, round final answers to the same number of significant digits as the given value with the fewest significant digits. Take extra care when rounding digits with multiple parts. You will see in this book that extra digits are carried in intermediate calculations. For more help with rounding, refer to the Skills Handbook in your textbook.

MAIN IDEA: Average speed is distance travelled divided by the time elapsed.

1. A cannonball flies through the air at a constant speed of 105 m/s for 2.4 s. How far does it travel? T/I

2. You drive to a city 552 km away, arriving precisely 5.00 h after departing. T/I
   (a) What was your average speed, in metres per second?

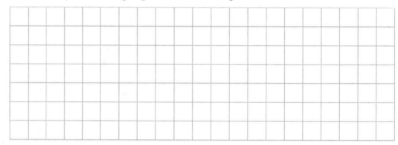

   (b) On the return trip, what will your average speed be, in metres per second, if you take a half-hour lunch break midway through the trip?

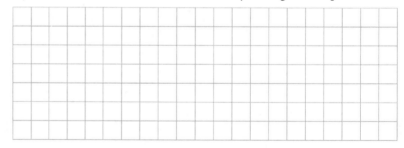

3. How many minutes does it take a snail, moving at 3.0 cm/min, to travel 72 cm? T/I

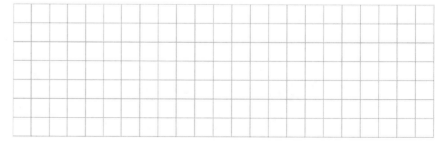

MAIN IDEA: Average velocity is the change in displacement divided by the time elapsed. On a position–time graph, average velocity is equal to the slope.

LEARNING TIP

Rate of Change
Average speed and average velocity are examples of rates of change—an important concept in science that describes how quickly a quantity is changing. Velocity is the rate of change of position, which means that the more rapidly an object's position is changing, the greater is the magnitude of its velocity.

4. A boat drifts eastward on a river. In 4.0 min, the boat has drifted 862 m. Calculate the boat's average velocity. T/I

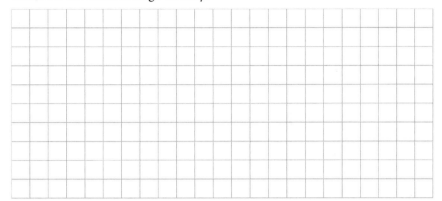

5. A skater skates west 70.0 m across a frozen river and realizes she has dropped her scarf. She skates back east 30.0 m to pick up her scarf, then 30.0 m west back to the other side. T/I

   (a) If she skates for 8.0 min, what is the skater's average velocity?

   (b) How does this compare with her average speed?

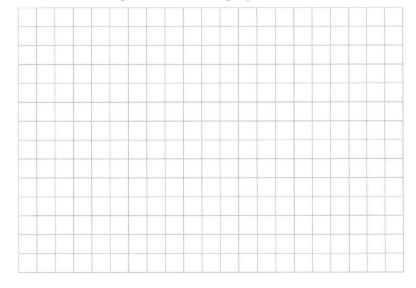

6. Identify the examples of motion in **Table 1** as uniform or non-uniform velocity. Explain your reasoning. K/U

Table 1 Describing Velocity: Uniform or Non-Uniform

Example	Uniform velocity	Non-uniform velocity	Explanation
A hockey puck moves smoothly across the ice at 6.5 m/s.			
A race car rounds a curved track at a steady 175 km/h.			
Light travels from a laser across an 8 m room where it reflects off a mirror.			
A planet orbits the Sun every 4.5 years.			

7. Describe a scenario that the motion in the graph in **Figure 1** could represent. T/I A

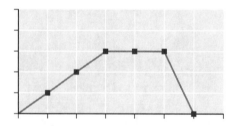

Figure 1

Acceleration

Vocabulary

acceleration ($\vec{a}_{av}$)

velocity–time graph

motion with uniform acceleration

instantaneous velocity ($\vec{v}_{inst}$)

Textbook pp. 21–30

MAIN IDEA: Acceleration is the rate of change in velocity.

1. A cannonball accelerates from rest to a muzzle speed of 150 m/s in 0.040 s. Calculate its average acceleration. ⬛T/I

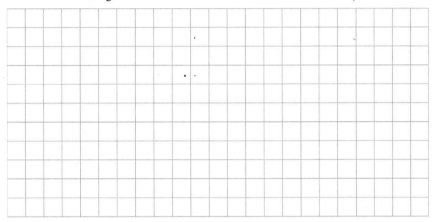

2. (a) A car is travelling at 25.0 m/s [S] and accelerates at 1.20 m/s² [S] for 3.00 s. Calculate the final velocity.

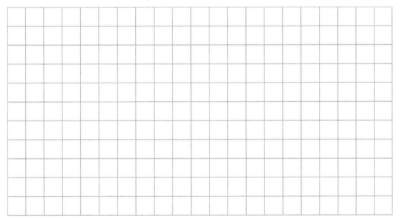

> **LEARNING TIP**
>
> **Square Seconds?**
> What is a square second? Good question! When we write acceleraton units as m/s², we are not implying that we have measured a square second. This is simply a shorter way of expressing the derived unit. You can also read the unit as "metres per second, per second"—describing how many metres per second of velocity are gained or lost during each second of acceleration.

(b) What is the final velocity of the car if the acceleration is 3.50 m/s² [N] for the same 3.00 s?

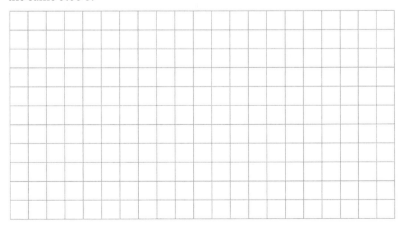

MAIN IDEA: Velocity–time graphs can be used to determine instantaneous velocity (value), acceleration (slope), and displacement (area).

3. The velocity of an object is shown in **Figure 1**. [T/I]

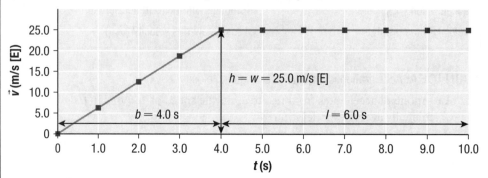

Velocity v. Time for a Complex Motion

$h = w = 25.0$ m/s [E]

$b = 4.0$ s

$l = 6.0$ s

Figure 1

LEARNING TIP

Slope and Area of Velocity–Time Graphs

The slope of a velocity–time graph gives the acceleration of the object. The area under a velocity–time graph gives the displacement of the object. Why is displacement related to the area under a velocity–time graph? One way to think about it is this: the greater the velocity during a given time interval, the greater the area under the graph, and the greater the displacement over that time interval.

(a) Calculate the object's displacement over the time interval 0.0 s to 10.0 s.

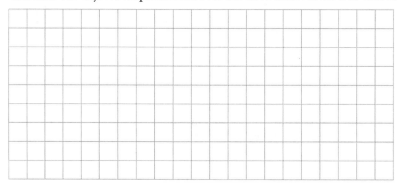

(b) Calculate the object's displacement over the time interval 2.0 s to 8.0 s.

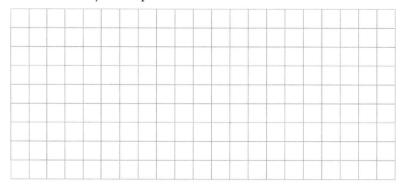

(c) What is the object's acceleration at $t = 4.0$ s and $t = 6.0$ s?

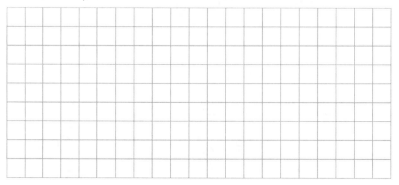

MAIN IDEA: Instantaneous velocity is the velocity of an object at a specific instant in time, or average velocity over an arbitrarily brief time interval. On a position–time graph, it is the slope of the curve. On a velocity–time graph, it is the value of the curve at any specific point in time.

4. The motion of an object is shown in **Figure 2**. K/U T/I

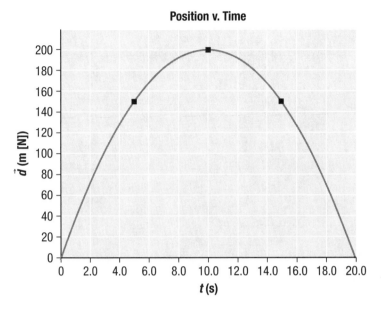

Position v. Time

Figure 2

(a) Determine the instantaneous velocity at $t = 0$ s, $t = 5$ s, and $t = 10$ s. Comment on the relationship between the average velocity over the first 10 s and the instantaneous velocity at 5 s.

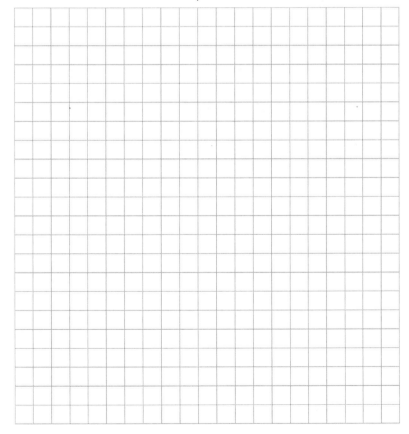

(b) Determine the instantaneous velocity at $t = 12$ s, $t = 15$ s, and $t = 18$ s. Plot these velocities, as well as those from part (a), on a velocity–time graph.

(c) Determine whether the object in Figure 2 is undergoing uniform acceleration. If the acceleration is uniform, determine its value. If it is not uniform, determine the acceleration at $t = 10$ s.

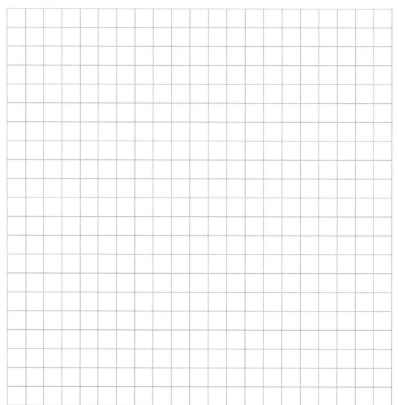

Comparing Graphs of Linear Motion

Textbook pp. 31–35

> **Vocabulary**
>
> acceleration–time graph

MAIN IDEA: The graphs of position–time, velocity–time, and acceleration–time provide different information about an object's motion, and are connected through slope and area.

1. The instantaneous velocity at time t_0 can be determined from a graph by
   (a) calculating the slope of the tangent line to the velocity–time graph at t_0.
   (b) calculating the area under the acceleration–time graph from 0 to t_0.
   (c) calculating the area under the position–time graph from 0 to t_0.
   (d) calculating the area under the velocity–time graph from 0 to t_0. K/U

2. What additional information must be given when converting an acceleration–time graph into a velocity–time graph, and when converting from velocity to position? K/U

3. The velocity–time graph in **Figure 1** represents the motion of a cheetah chasing prey. T/I

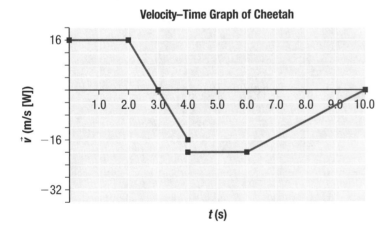

Velocity–Time Graph of Cheetah

Figure 1

   (a) At what time(s) does the cheetah have zero velocity?

   (b) What is the cheetah's instantaneous velocity at $t = 2$ s?

(c) What is the instantaneous velocity at $t = 7$ s?

(d) From the velocity–time graph, construct a graph of the cheetah's acceleration.

4. Use the acceleration–time graph in **Figure 2** to generate velocity and time data for the object. Then use this information to construct a velocity–time graph. T/I A

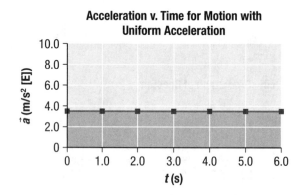

Figure 2

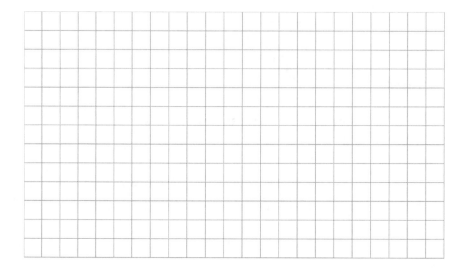

Five Key Equations for Motion with Uniform Acceleration

Textbook pp. 36–39

MAIN IDEA: Motion with uniform acceleration can be described with five key equations. Each equation can be distinguished by what it does *not* involve.

Table 1 The Five Key Equations of Accelerated Motion

	Equation	Variables found in equation	Variables not in equation
Equation 1	$\Delta \vec{d} = \left[\dfrac{\vec{v}_f + \vec{v}_i}{2} \right] \Delta t$	$\Delta \vec{d}, \Delta t, \vec{v}_f, \vec{v}_i$	$\vec{a}_{av}$
Equation 2	$\vec{v}_f = \vec{v}_i + \vec{a}_{av} \Delta t$	$\vec{a}_{av}, \Delta t, \vec{v}_f, \vec{v}_i$	$\Delta \vec{d}$
Equation 3	$\Delta \vec{d} = \vec{v}_i \Delta t + \dfrac{1}{2} \vec{a}_{av} \Delta t^2$	$\Delta \vec{d}, \vec{a}_{av}, \Delta t, \vec{v}_i$	$\vec{v}_f$
Equation 4	$v_f^2 = v_i^2 + 2 a_{av} \Delta d$	$\Delta d, a_{av}, v_f, v_i$	Δt
Equation 5	$\Delta \vec{d} = \vec{v}_f \Delta t - \dfrac{1}{2} \vec{a}_{av} \Delta t^2$	$\Delta \vec{d}, \vec{a}_{av}, \Delta t, \vec{v}_f$	$\vec{v}_i$

Interpreting Areas Under a Motion Graph
Notice that the rectangular area (area 2) in Figure 1 represents the displacement the object would have undergone had it continued at constant velocity $\vec{v}_i$. The triangular area (area 1) represents the extra displacement the object experienced due to its acceleration.

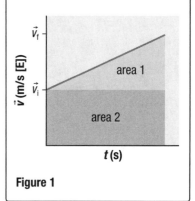

Figure 1

1. As a driver's vehicle approaches an intersection at 20 m/s [N], the driver applies the brakes, creating a uniform acceleration of 2.5 m/s² [S]. **K/U** **T/I**

   (a) Identify the equation that you would use to obtain the time it takes for the driver to come to a stop; then calculate the time required to stop.

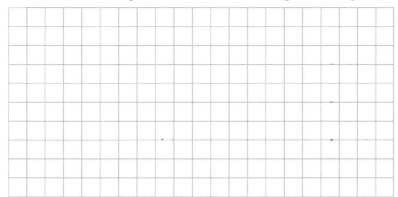

   (b) Identify the equation that you would use to obtain the distance the vehicle travels before stopping; then calculate the distance travelled.

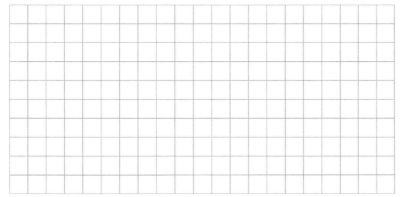

2. A forensic scientist tests a gun's muzzle velocity by firing a bullet into a vat of ballistics gel. If the bullet comes to a complete stop 33 cm into the gel after 2.0 ms, how fast was it travelling before entering the gel? T/I

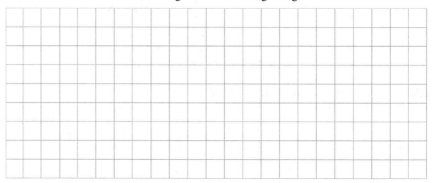

3. As a traffic light turns green, a car at rest begins to move forward at a uniform acceleration of 3.1 m/s² [E]. At the same time, a truck passes through the intersection travelling at a constant velocity of 15 m/s [E]. T/I

(a) Calculate the displacement of the car and the truck after 2.0 s and after 8.0 s.

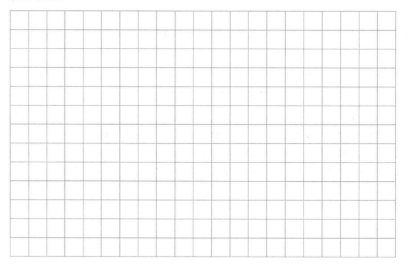

(b) At what time does the truck pass the car and the car pass the truck?

(c) How far down the road does the truck pass the car and the car pass the truck?

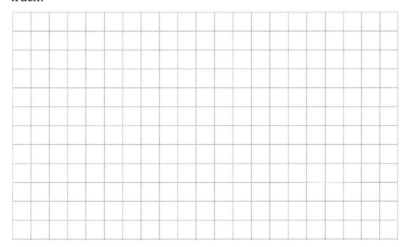

4. A basketball is thrown at 8.00 m/s [up] from a height of 2.00 m and eventually comes back down to hit the floor. T/I

(a) Assuming a uniform acceleration of 9.80 m/s² [down], how long was the ball in flight?

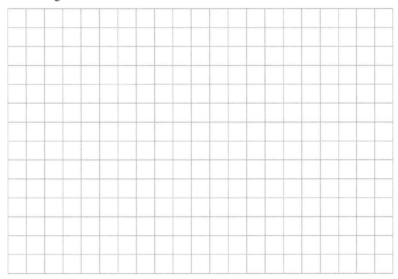

(b) Calculate the ball's velocity immediately prior to hitting the floor.

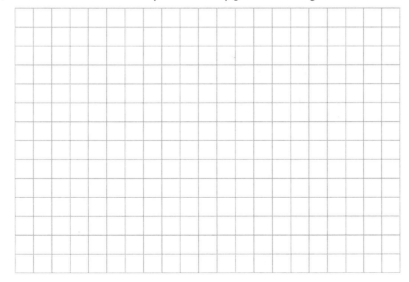

Acceleration Near Earth's Surface

> **Vocabulary**
>
> acceleration due to gravity (g)   terminal velocity
>
> free fall

MAIN IDEA: In the absence of other forces, objects near Earth's surface accelerate downward at $g = 9.8$ m/s². Vertical directions are typically denoted by positive (up) and negative (down). Air resistance can cause objects to accelerate at values less than g.

1. A coin is tossed up in the air and reaches its maximum height of 1.0 m after 2.0 s. Which of the following is the acceleration of the coin at $t = 2.0$ s? T/I
   (a) zero
   (b) 9.8 m/s²
   (c) −9.8 m/s²
   (d) 0.75 m/s²

2. A stone is dropped from rest off a bridge 20.0 m above the water. T/I
   (a) How long does the stone fall until it hits the water?

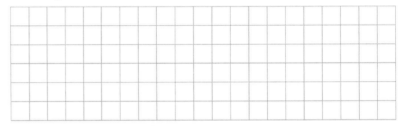

   (b) How fast is the stone falling at $t = 0.50$ s, at $t = 1.50$ s, and at impact?

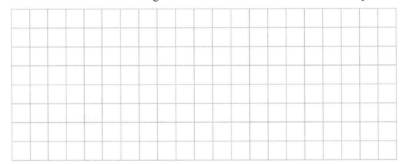

3. A cannon shell is fired straight up in the air. Assume the shell is fired with an initial velocity of 325 m/s from a height of 2.4 m, and neglect air resistance. K/U T/I
   (a) To what height will the shell rise?

(b) How long will the shell be in the air?

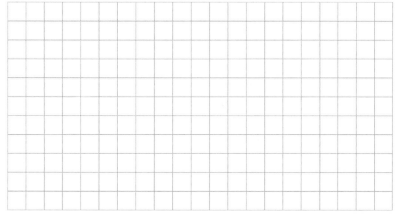

(c) What will be the shell's final velocity immediately before hitting the ground?

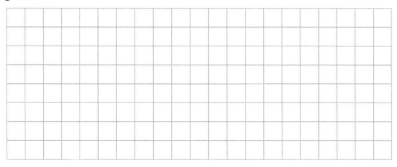

(d) Is the shell's acceleration ever zero?

(e) In this scenario, air resistance was neglected. If you take air resistance into account, predict how the actual flight time, final speed, and acceleration would differ.

4. (a) A rubber ball is dropped from a height of 2.0 m, and on the bounce returns to a height of 1.6 m. Determine the velocity of the ball immediately before bouncing and its velocity immediately afterward. How do the speeds at these two points compare?

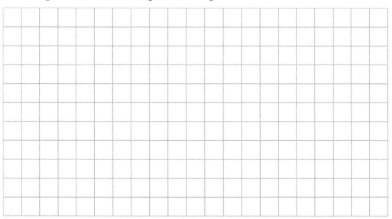

(b) Sketch a velocity–time graph and a position–time graph for the rubber ball. K/U T/I

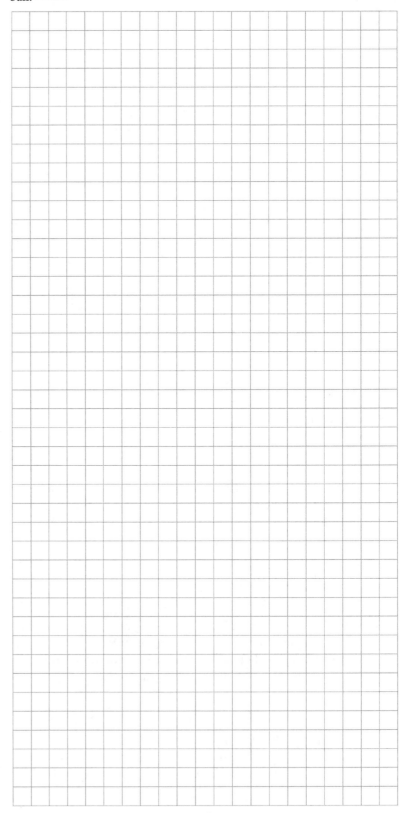

Electronic Speed Limiters for Teen Drivers

Textbook pp. 44–45

MAIN IDEA: Electronic speed limiters help increase vehicle safety, improve fuel efficiency, and reduce the environmental impact of vehicles.

1. What is an electronic speed limiter? Explain. K/U

2. By how much does speed affect traffic fatalities and fuel consumption? K/U

MAIN IDEA: Support your position on an issue based on research and analysis of alternative positions.

3. Use a graphic organizer, such as the comparison matrix in **Table 1**, to organize different positions on the issue of electronic speed limiters for teen drivers. K/U C

Table 1 Views on Electronic Speed Limiters for Teens

For	Against	Recommendation

STUDY TIP

Comparison Matrix
You can use a graphic organizer such as a comparison matrix to organize different factors and opinions on an issue.

MAIN IDEA: Communicate your position on an issue clearly and effectively.

4. Write a brief position statement addressed to your student government about your views on the issue of electronic speed limiters for teen drivers. C A

Motion in a Straight Line

The graphic organizer below summarizes the main ideas from Chapter 1. As you progress through the course, consider making your own graphic organizers to take notes and study. Fill in the missing information in this graphic organizer to complete the summary.

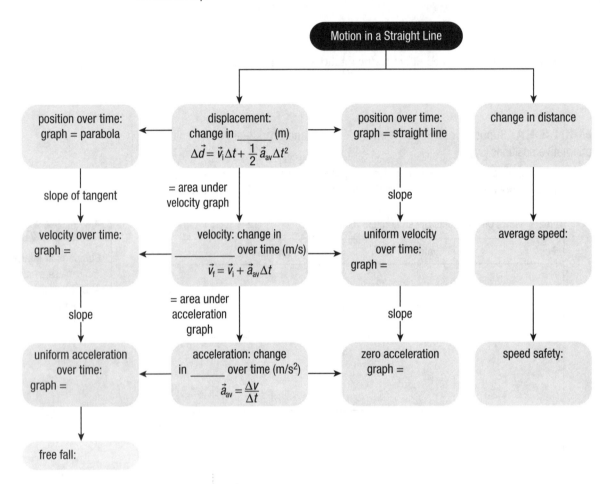

1. An object is travelling due east at a constant velocity. Which of the following describes its position–time graph? (1.2) **K/U**
   (a) The graph is a horizontal line above the *x*-axis.
   (b) The graph is a horizontal line below the *x*-axis.
   (c) The graph is a straight line with positive slope.
   (d) The graph is a straight line with negative slope.

2. Indicate whether each statement if true or false. If you think the statement is false, rewrite it to make it true. **K/U**
   (a) The area under the graph of the position–time graph can be interpreted as the velocity of a moving object. (1.4)

   (b) Electronic speed limiters have been used to reduce highway emissions from trucks. (1.7)

3. Using (a) algebraic methods and (b) scale diagrams, determine the total displacement of motion described by $\Delta \vec{d}_1 = 30.0$ m [N]; $\Delta \vec{d}_2 = 15.0$ m [S]. (1.1) **T/I**

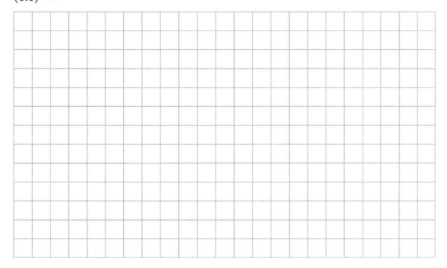

4. A player kicks a soccer ball with an initial velocity of 2.0 m/s [E]. In 0.50 s, the ball has a velocity of 8.0 m/s [W]. Calculate the average acceleration of the ball. (1.3) **T/I**

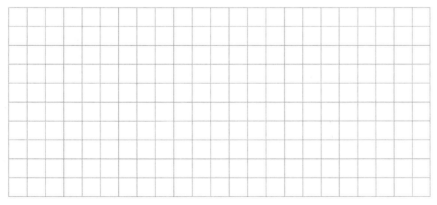

K/U Knowledge/Understanding
T/I Thinking/Investigation
C Communication
A Application

Table 1 The Five Key Equations of
Accelerated Motion

	Equation
Equation 1	$\Delta \vec{d} = \left[\dfrac{\vec{v}_f + \vec{v}_i}{2} \right] \Delta t$
Equation 2	$\vec{v}_f = \vec{v}_i + \vec{a}_{av} \Delta t$
Equation 3	$\Delta \vec{d} = \vec{v}_i \Delta t + \dfrac{1}{2} \vec{a}_{av} \Delta t^2$
Equation 4	$v_f^2 = v_i^2 + 2a_{av} \Delta d$
Equation 5	$\Delta \vec{d} = \vec{v}_f \Delta t - \dfrac{1}{2} \vec{a}_{av} \Delta t^2$

5. A motorcyclist accelerates after he passes a restaurant. At time $t = 0$, he is 4.0 m [E] of the restaurant. Four seconds later, he is moving east at 15 m/s. His acceleration is a constant 3.0 m/s². Choose the appropriate equations from **Table 1** to answer the following questions. (1.5) T/I

   (a) Calculate his initial velocity.

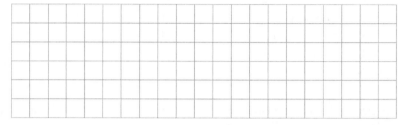

   (b) What is his position after 4.0 s relative to the restaurant?

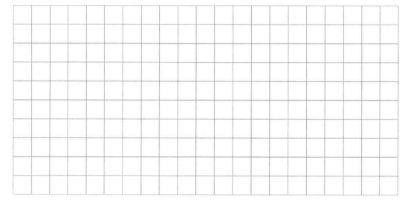

6. At the completion of a baseball inning, the pitcher throws a baseball straight up in the air at an initial velocity of 7.0 m/s. (1.5, 1.6) T/I

   (a) How high does the ball go (from where it is thrown)?

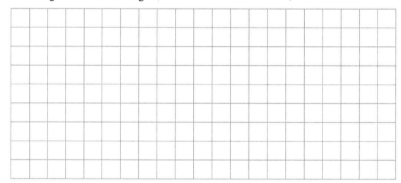

   (b) When does it reach that height?

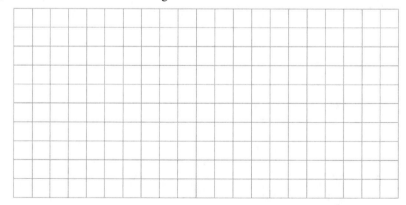

Motion in Two Dimensions— A Scale Diagram Approach

Textbook pp. 60–65

Vocabulary

resultant vector

MAIN IDEA: Objects can move in two dimensions, such as horizontal and vertical planes, and a compass rose can be used to express directions in a horizontal plane.

1. The vector 12 [W 25° S] is identical to which vector? **K/U**

   (a) 12 [W 25° N]   (c) 24 [S 25° W]

   (b) 12 [S 65° W]   (d) 12 [E 65° S]

2. Draw vectors on the compass rose in **Figure 1** with the following directions: **K/U** **T/I**

   (a) [E 35° S]   (d) [S 5° E]

   (b) [N 50° W]   (e) [S 45° W]

   (c) [E 80° N]   (f) [E 32° N]

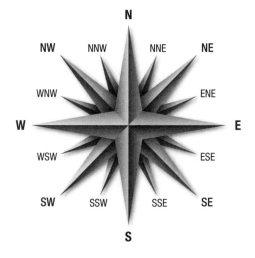

Figure 1

3. Draw a scale diagram of the displacement vector $\Delta \vec{d} = 26$ m [E 40° N]. **K/U** **T/I**

MAIN IDEA: To determine the total displacement of a movement in two dimensions, add displacement vectors together using a scale diagram, joining the vectors tip to tail. The resultant vector extends from the tail of the first vector to the tip of the last vector.

4. The vectors $\Delta \vec{d}_1$ and $\Delta \vec{d}_2$ represent motions of an object in two dimensions. A student drew the vector diagram in **Figure 2(a)** to determine the sum of the two vectors. K/U T/I C

   (a) What mistake do you see in the diagram?

   (b) Explain how you can correct the mistake. Draw the sum of vectors $\Delta \vec{d}_1$ and $\Delta \vec{d}_2$ in the space provided in **Figure 2(b)**.

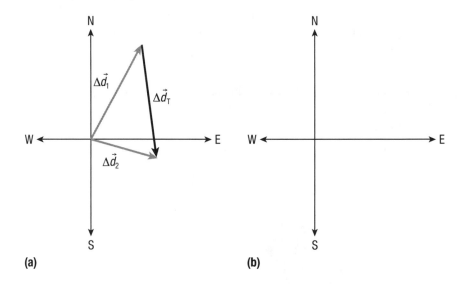

(a)   (b)

Figure 2

   (c) Does your corrected drawing change the resultant vector $\Delta \vec{d}_T$ in any way? Explain your answer.

5. A soccer player runs due east from the centre of a soccer field for 18 m. Then she turns and travels 30 m [N 70° W]. Draw the resultant vector diagram to determine her total displacement. T/I

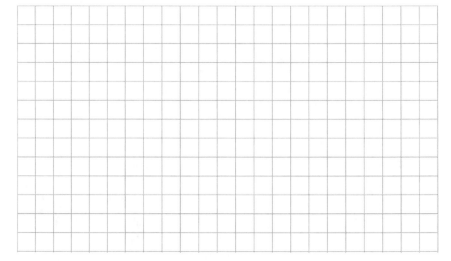

6. An ant travels 185 mm [W 15° S]. Then the ant turns and walks in a different direction, travelling 240 mm [N 60° E] in 14 s.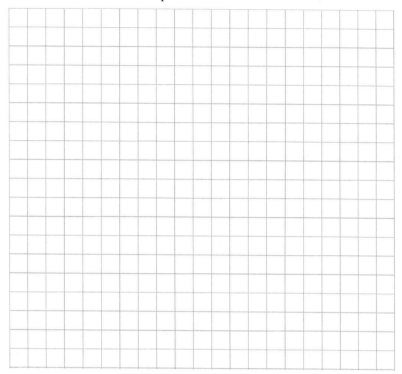

    (a) Determine the ant's total displacement.

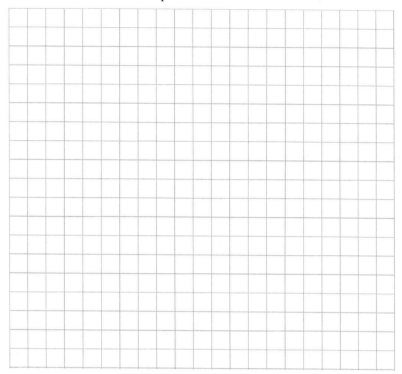

    (b) Calculate the ant's average velocity.

7. Suppose two vectors are added. Under what conditions would the sum of the magnitudes of the vectors equal the magnitude of the resultant vector?

Motion in Two Dimensions—An Algebraic Approach

> **Vocabulary**
>
> component vector

MAIN IDEA: Using the component method of vector addition, the Pythagorean theorem, and the tangent function, all vector addition problems can be converted into a problem involving two perpendicular vectors.

1. Is the following statement true or false? If you think the statement is false, rewrite it to make it true. Solving problems that involve motion in two dimensions using vector scale diagrams is more precise than using an algebraic solution method. K/U

2. Use the _____ to calculate the magnitude of the sum of two perpendicular vectors, and use the tangent function to determine the _____ of the resultant vector. K/U

3. Break down the vector $\Delta \vec{d}_1 = 32.00$ m [W 35° S] into its perpendicular components. Draw them on the coordinate system in **Figure 1**, and show your work below. T/I

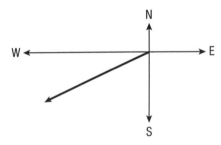

Figure 1

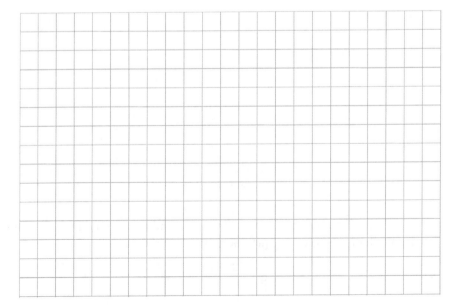

4. A model car travels 25.0 m due east, then turns and travels 18.0 m [W 40° N]. Determine the car's total displacement, and draw the resultant vector.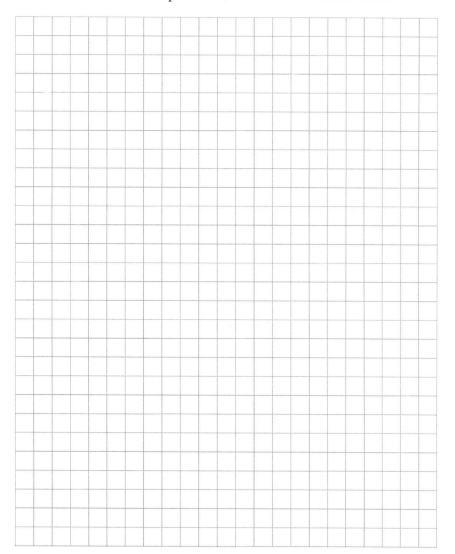

MAIN IDEA: River crossing problems involve independent motions in horizontal and vertical directions.

5. (a) A 0.6 km-wide river flows with a velocity of 20.0 km/h [E]. A boat leaves a boat launch travelling at 15 km/h in a due north direction. Calculate how long it will take the boat to cross the river, in hours. See **Figure 2**.

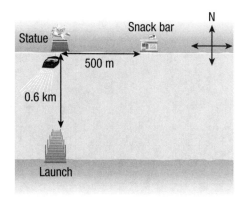

Figure 2

2.2 Motion in Two Dimensions—An Algebraic Approach

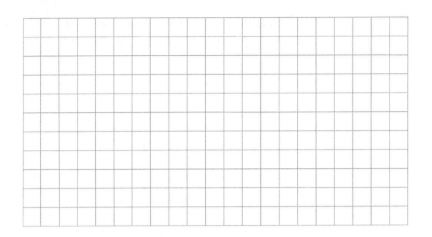

(b) The passengers in the boat want to reach the statue on the far side of the river. If they steer the boat due north for the entire trip, will they arrive at the statue? Explain. K/U

(c) If they steer the boat due north for the entire trip, will the boat land east or west of the snack bar? Calculate the distance, in metres, east or west of the snack bar that the boat will land. T/I

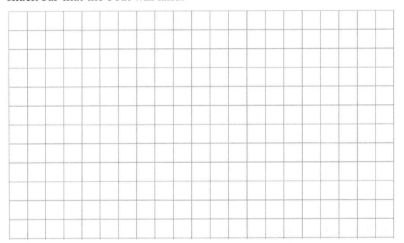

(d) Calculate the resultant velocity at which an observer standing at the snack bar would see the boat travelling. Include a vector diagram in your answer. T/I

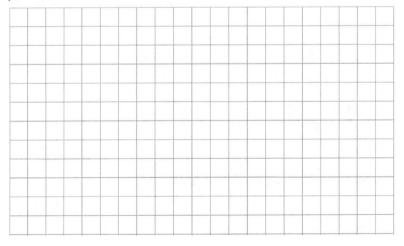

Projectile Motion

Textbook pp. 76–81

Vocabulary

projectile

projectile motion

time of flight

range

MAIN IDEA: Horizontal motion and vertical motion for a projectile are independent of each other. Projectiles move at constant velocity in the horizontal direction and with constant acceleration due to the force of gravity in the vertical direction.

1. Is the following statement true or false? If you think the statement is false, rewrite it to make it true. A projectile in mid-flight has two forces acting on it: gravity and a horizontal force. **K/U**

2. Two archers shoot arrows horizontally at an angle that is parallel to the ground. The initial horizontal velocity of arrow 1 is twice the horizontal velocity of arrow 2. Which statement is true? **K/U**
   (a) Arrow 1 will hit the ground before arrow 2.
   (b) Arrow 2 will hit the ground before arrow 1.
   (c) Arrow 1 and arrow 2 will hit the ground at the same time.
   (d) Both arrows will hit the ground when their horizontal velocity is zero.

3. In **Figure 1**, two beanbags are thrown out the window from the top floor of a building. Beanbag A is dropped, and beanbag B is projected horizontally. **K/U**

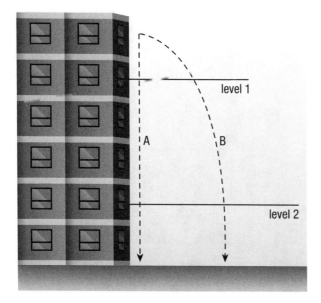

level 1

A   B

level 2

Figure 1

   (a) At level 1, which beanbag is falling downward faster, and which beanbag is travelling at a greater velocity?

   (b) At which level is beanbag B travelling with greater horizontal velocity?

> ### LEARNING **TIP**
>
> **x, y, and t**
> In projectile motion problems, it is helpful to remember that time, t, is a scalar variable and is different from either the x-variable or the y-variable describing the two-dimensional vectors of displacement, velocity, and acceleration.

(c) At which level is beanbag A travelling with greater velocity? Explain.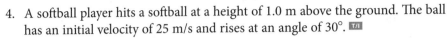

4. A softball player hits a softball at a height of 1.0 m above the ground. The ball has an initial velocity of 25 m/s and rises at an angle of 30°. T/I

(a) Draw and label a diagram showing the components of the initial velocity of the softball.

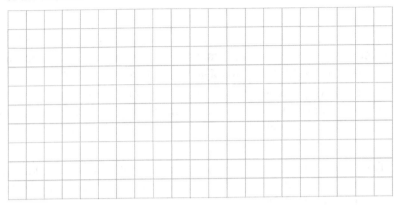

(b) An outfielder catches the ball at a height of 1.0 m above the ground. How long does the ball stay in flight?

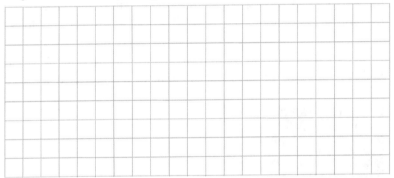

(c) How far does the ball travel horizontally?

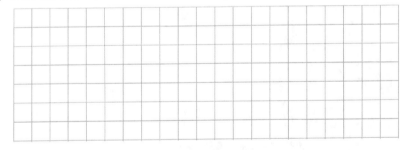

(d) Calculate the maximum height of the ball.

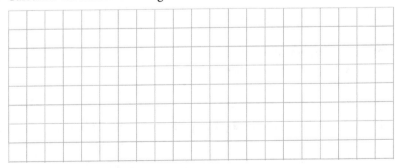

5. A child throws a stone at an initial velocity of 15 m/s and an angle of 45° up and out into the water as shown in **Figure 2**. T/I

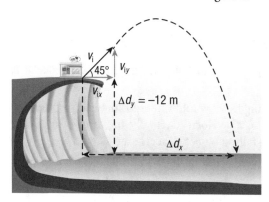

Figure 2

(a) How far from the child does the stone land?

(b) Calculate the final velocity of the stone just before it hits the water.

Physics JOURNAL

Galileo Galilei: Sixteenth-Century "New Scientist"

MAIN IDEA: Galileo performed experiments that proved that all falling objects accelerate at the same rate.

1. According to Aristotle, a falling body would undergo "natural" motion and travel at a _____ velocity. Actually, the force of _____ causes a falling object to accelerate. **K/U**

2. To prove that falling objects were accelerating, what did Galileo need to show? **K/U**
   (a) that two objects with different masses fell to the ground at the same rate
   (b) that the distance a falling object travelled doubled during each second that it fell
   (c) that the distance a falling object travelled was constant during each second that it fell
   (d) that heavier objects did not fall at the same rate as lighter objects

3. (a) Complete **Table 1** for a falling object. The term Δt represents elapsed time from the beginning of the fall, and Δd represents the total distance from the top.

   Table 1 Distance Travelled By a Falling Object

Δt (s)	$\Delta d = \dfrac{1}{2}\vec{a}_{av}\,\Delta t^2$	Δd (m, from top)	Δd (m, from previous value)
0		0	0
1.0			
2.0			
3.0			
4.0			
5.0			

Figure 1

0 m

20 m

40 m

60 m

80 m

100 m

120 m

140 m

   (b) Show the distances from **Table 1** on **Figure 1**.

   (c) Describe the pattern that you see in **Figure 1**.

   (d) Examine the pattern in the last column of **Table 1**, the difference between values. What does this pattern indicate? **K/U** **T/I** **C**

Explore Applications in Kinematics

Accelerometers: Accelerating Your Life

Textbook pp. 84–85

MAIN IDEA: By measuring acceleration, accelerometers provide a means to navigate, stabilize, and control movement in a wide variety of real-world applications.

1. Is the following statement true or false? If the statement is false, rewrite it to make it true. Accelerometers are tiny devices that measure how fast an object is moving in a certain direction or directions. **K/U**

2. Which of the following best describes an accelerometer? **K/U**
   (a) a device that is used to change the speed of a moving object
   (b) a device made of semi-conducting materials a few decimetres long
   (c) a device that can be used to measure the tilt and movement of an object
   (d) a device that accelerates the motion shown on a video screen

3. Use **Table 1** to consider factors involved in evaluating the impact of devices with accelerometers. **K/U** **T/I** **A**

Table 1 Possible Impacts of Accelerometers

Factor	Advantages/Disadvantages

Motion in Two Dimensions

Use the graphic organizers below to summarize what you have learned about the motion of objects in two dimensions and projectile motion. Fill in the blanks and write additional notes to help you review the concepts in this chapter.

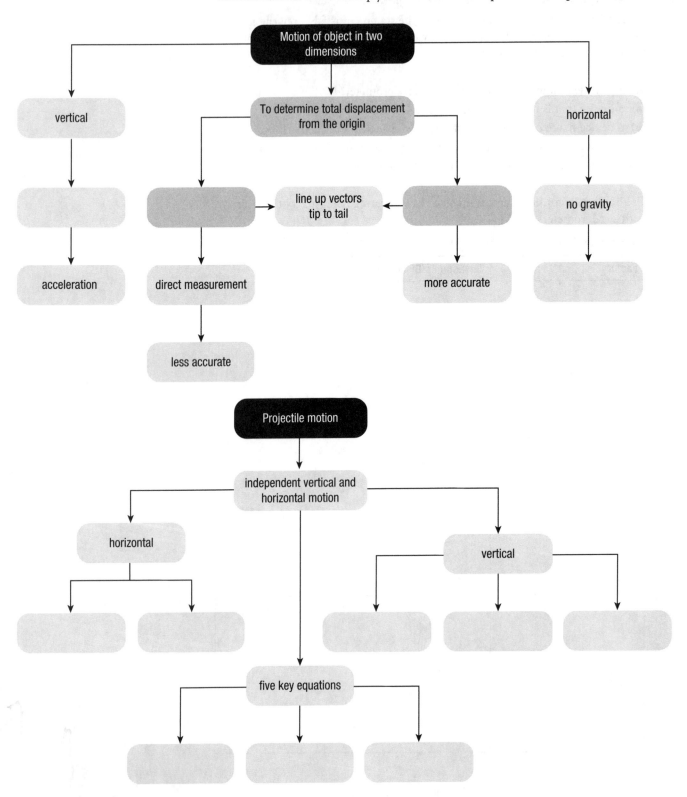

1. Galileo proved that the motion of an object in _____ does not depend on the _____ of the object. (2.4) **K/U**

2. A boat sails 40 m [E 20° S]. Then the boat turns, travelling 54 m [N 24° W]. The two displacements take 1.3 min. (2.1) **T/I**

   (a) Use a scale diagram approach to determine the boat's total displacement.

   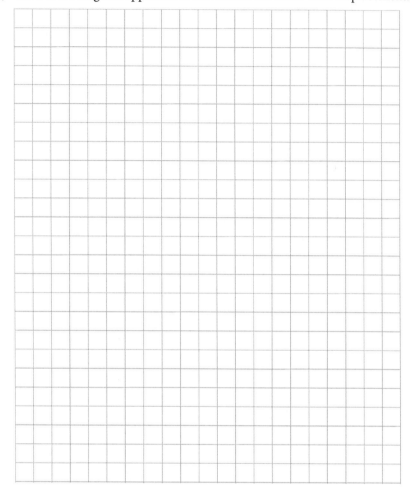

   (b) Calculate the boat's average velocity.

   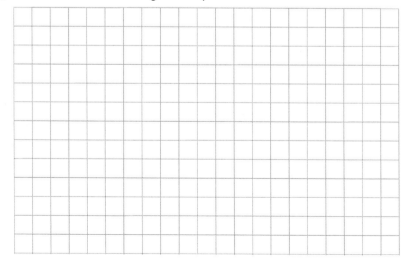

K/U	Knowledge/Understanding
T/I	Thinking/Investigation
C	Communication
A	Application

3. A rabbit travels 20.0 m [W 65° N], then turns and travels 25 m [E 25° N]. Use an algebraic approach to determine the rabbit's total displacement. Draw the vectors and label the diagram. (2.2) T/I

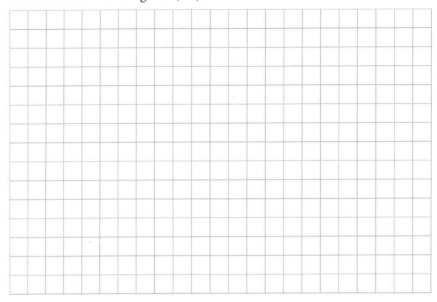

4. (a) A hockey player on a frozen lake shoots a puck with an initial velocity of 40.0 m/s that rises at an angle of 20°. Draw and label a diagram showing the components of the initial velocity of the puck.

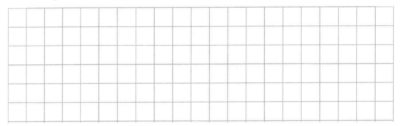

(b) How long does the puck stay in flight?

(c) How far does the puck travel horizontally?

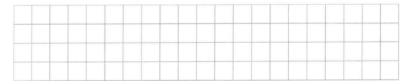

(d) Calculate the maximum height of the puck. (2.3) T/I

1. Which of the following describes the relationship in the equation
   $\Delta\vec{d} = \frac{1}{2}\vec{a}_{av}\Delta t^2$? (1.5, 1.6) **K/U**

	K/U	Knowledge/Understanding
	T/I	Thinking/Investigation
	C	Communication
	A	Application

   (a) Change in displacement is proportional to the change in time.
   (b) Change in displacement is proportional to the change in time squared.
   (c) Change in displacement is proportional to the average acceleration.
   (d) Change in displacement is proportional to the average acceleration squared.

2. In river crossing problems, the horizontal and vertical velocities are constant. In projectile motion problems,
   (a) the horizontal and vertical velocities are also both constant.
   (b) the horizontal velocity changes while the vertical velocity is constant.
   (c) the horizontal velocity is constant while the vertical velocity changes.
   (d) the horizontal and vertical velocities both change. (1.6, 2.3) **K/U**

3. Indicate whether each statement is true or false. If you think the statement is false, rewrite it to make it true. **K/U**
   (a) If a bee flies 3.1 m [E] to a flower and then 4.9 m [W] to its hive, the total displacement is 8.0 m [W]. (1.1)

   (b) An accelerometer is a device that accelerates electrons in a laboratory experiment. (2.5)

4. Name two results of installing an electronic speed delimiter in your vehicle. (1.7) **K/U**

5. Explain the role of Galileo's experiments in developing the equation
   $\Delta\vec{d} = \frac{1}{2}\vec{a}_{av}\Delta t^2$. (2.4) **K/U**

6. **Figure 1** shows a graph of complex motion. Which part of the graph shows an object with uniform acceleration? (1.2, 1.3, 1.4) K/U T/I

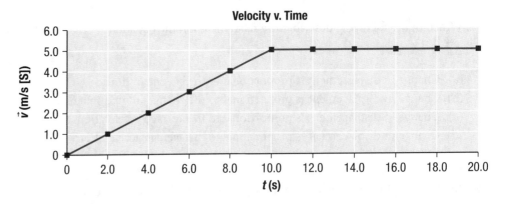

Figure 1

7. A fisherman is paddling east across a pond in his canoe to get to his favourite fishing spot. The velocity of the canoe is 0.40 km/h [E]. The stream's current has a velocity of 0.30 km/h [S]. The pond is 50.0 m wide. (2.2) T/I

   (a) How many minutes does it take the canoe to cross the pond?

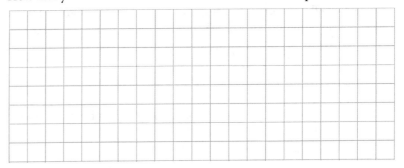

   (b) How far from the fishing spot does the canoe land on the other side of the pond?

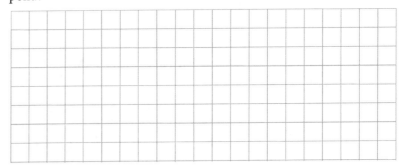

   (c) What is the canoe's resultant velocity, in kilometres/hour? T/I

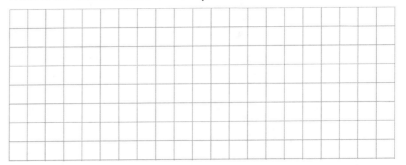

Chapter 3: Newton's Laws of Motion

A force often is described simply as a push or a pull. Force is a vector quantity with both a direction and a magnitude. The effect of forces on the motion of objects is described by Newton's three laws of motion. Newton's first law states that if the net force acting on an object is zero, then that object will remain at rest or continue to move at constant speed in a straight line. Newton's first law is the same as Galileo's law of inertia. Inertia is a property of matter that resists change in motion.

Newton's second law states that if a net force acts on an object, then the object will accelerate. This acceleration will be proportional to the net force, in the same direction as the net force, and inversely proportional to the object's mass.

Newton's third law states that for every action force, there is a simultaneous reaction force that is equal in magnitude but opposite in direction.

Newton's three laws that describe how the net force affects acceleration can be combined with the kinematics equations to describe how the applied net force affects position and speed.

Chapter 4: Applications of Forces

Gravity and friction commonly are involved in applications of Newton's laws. An object's weight is the gravitational force exerted on it and depends on the strength of the gravitational field at the location of the object. Unlike weight, the mass of an object is an unchangeable property that measures the amount of matter it contains.

If gravity alone acts on an object, it accelerates on Earth at about 9.8 m/s^2. Falling objects usually also experience an air resistance force proportional to speed, until the object reaches a terminal speed where air resistance balances gravity.

Static friction keeps one object from sliding over another by providing a friction force that adjusts to balance the applied force, up until a maximum force of static friction. This maximum force has been found experimentally to be proportional to the normal force between the surfaces. In contrast, kinetic friction opposes the motion of moving objects. Sliding friction is kinetic friction of two surfaces sliding on each other, and is also proportional to the normal force. The proportionality constants for static and for sliding friction depend on the characteristics of the surfaces.

The properties of mass, weight, and friction, combined with Newton's laws of motion, are applied in automotive technology, sports technology, the design of medical devices, and other technological uses.

BIG IDEAS

- Forces can change the motion of an object.
- Applications of Newton's laws of motion have led to technological developments that affect society and the environment.

Types of Forces

Textbook pp. 114–122

Vocabulary

dynamics	free-body diagram (FBD)	normal force ($\vec{F}_N$)	net force ($\vec{F}_{net}$)
newton (N)	applied force ($\vec{F}_a$)	friction ($\vec{F}_f$)	
system diagram	tension ($\vec{F}_T$)	force of gravity ($\vec{F}_g$)	

MAIN IDEA: A force is a push or a pull. Force is a vector quantity, and the total force, or net force, acting on an object determines the effect of the forces on the object's motion. A free-body diagram is used to help determine the net force on an object.

1. How does kinematics differ from dynamics? K/U

2. The SI unit of force is the _____ . The symbol used for force is the _____ . K/U

3. How does a system diagram differ from a free-body diagram? K/U

STUDY TIP

Free-Body Diagrams
Sketching a free-body diagram is a good way to visualize the forces acting on an object.

---

4. Suppose two students are pushing a crate horizontally along the ground. Draw the free-body diagram for the crate, and label each force acting on it. C

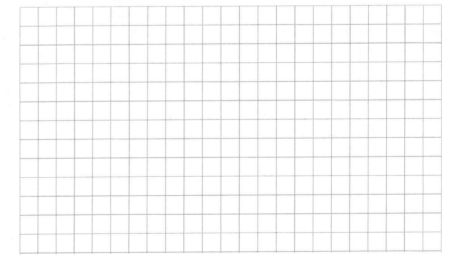

5. Suppose several forces act on a single object. Define each of these terms in your own words: K/U

   (a) applied force:

   (b) net force:

STUDY TIP

When Many Forces Act
There may be many forces acting on one object. The vector sum of all the forces, which is the net force, is always what determines how the forces affect the motion of an object.

6. Complete **Table 1** describing what characterizes each type of force. K/U

   Table 1 Common Forces

	Force	Identifying feature	Direction
(a)	friction	opposes motion of one surface past another	
(b)	normal force		perpendicular to a surface
(c)		pulling force exerted by a string, rope, or cable	along a string, rope, or cable
(d)		force of attraction to Earth, proportional to object's mass	

7. An object is in free fall when the only force acting on it is _____. K/U

8. (a) What is a contact force?

STUDY TIP

Calculating the Force of Gravity
To calculate the magnitude of the force of gravity on an object, use the equation $\vec{F}_g = m\vec{g}$ where $g = 9.8$ m/s^2 [down].

   (b) Give two examples of non-contact forces. K/U

9. When an object with a mass of 0.50 kg hangs from a spring scale, the spring scale should indicate a force of _____. K/U

10. Draw the free-body diagram for a block of wood resting on a board that makes an angle of 30° with the horizontal direction. The force of friction, $\vec{F}_f$, keeps the block of wood from sliding. C A

11. The following free-body diagram (**Figure 1**) illustrates the forces acting on a boat weighing 800 N as it floats in the water, with a 630 N passenger and a 590 N passenger. Determine the upward force $\vec{F}_{water}$ that the water exerts to support the boat so that the net force is zero. ᴛ/ɪ

Figure 1

MAIN IDEA: There are four categories of forces called the four fundamental forces: the gravitational force, the electromagnetic force, the strong nuclear force, and the weak nuclear force.

12. Complete **Table 2** with descriptions of the four fundamental forces. ᴋ/ᴜ

Table 2 The Fundamental Forces

	Fundamental force	Description
(a)	gravitational	keeps planets in orbit and pulls objects toward Earth's centre
(b)	electromagnetic	
(c)	strong nuclear	
(d)	weak nuclear	

Newton's First Law of Motion

Vocabulary		Textbook pp. 123–129
inertia	first law of motion	

MAIN IDEA: Newton's first law states that without a net force, there is no change in motion; any object at rest will remain at rest, and any object in motion will simply continue moving at constant velocity.

1. The inertia of an object is its tendency to resist _____. K/U

2. Describe what Galileo argued about the motion of an object in the absence of friction. K/U

3. State Newton's first law of motion in your own words. K/U

4. Is the following statement true or false? If the statement is false, rewrite it to make it true: A non-zero force can start only an object in motion, speed it up, or slow it down. K/U

5. You place a book on the dashboard of a car, intending to read it later. As the car speeds up, the book appears to fall backwards into the seat. Explain, in terms of inertia, the actual motion of the book and what causes it to appear to act as it does. T/I

6. You are riding in a car at constant speed and put your book on the back seat. The car turns sharply to the right. How will the book move relative to the inside of the car? Explain your reasoning in terms of the book's inertia. T/I

STUDY TIP

Inertia in Physics and Daily Life
In everyday language, people often use the term "inertia" to describe a state of inactivity. In physics, inertia includes resistance to stopping, starting, changing direction while in motion, or any other change in motion.

STUDY TIP

Say It in Other Words
When you read a statement of a law or principle, it helps to try rewording it in more familiar language, and to think of some familiar examples.

7. Complete **Table 1**, listing what each observation implies about whether a net force acts on a moving object. [A]

Table 1 Effects of Force

	Observation	Is a net force acting on the object?
(a)	The object remains at rest.	
(b)	The object begins moving.	
(c)	The object speeds up.	
(d)	The object slows down.	
(e)	The moving object turns to the right.	
(f)	The object remains in motion, travelling in the same direction at constant speed.	

8. The net force acting on a block of wood is zero. The block rests on a table and experiences a friction force that keeps it from moving, an applied force of 2.0 N pushing it, a gravitational force of 10.2 N, and a normal force of 10.2 N. The block does not move. [T/I] [C]

(a) Draw the free-body diagram for this situation.

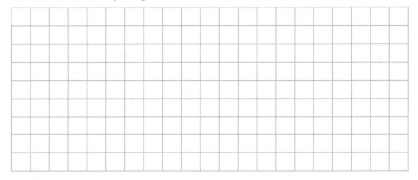

(b) Determine the force of friction acting on the block using Newton's first law. Explain your reasoning.

9. Two students are pushing a wheeled cart forwards along the level ground at a constant velocity. The students are both pushing the same side of the cart. One student exerts a force of 21 N on the cart and the other student exerts a force of 25 N on the cart. The cart also experiences a force of friction. [T/I] [C]

(a) Draw the free-body diagram for the cart.

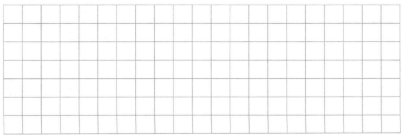

(b) What net force acts on the cart? Explain.

(c) Calculate the force of friction. Show your calculation and explain your answer in words.

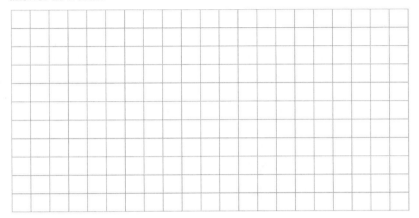

10. A car moving at 30 km/h collides with the rear of a stationary vehicle. K/U
    (a) Using Newton's first law, explain what will happen to a person in the moving vehicle if they are not wearing a seat belt when the vehicle comes to a sudden stop.

    (b) Explain how the use of seat belts reduces the likelihood of injury if this happens.

11. Explain, in terms of Newton's laws, why blood might tend to accumulate in an astronaut's legs during the rapid acceleration of a space launch. K/U A

Newton's Second Law of Motion

> **Vocabulary**
> second law of motion

MAIN IDEA: When a net force acts on an object, the magnitude of the resulting acceleration depends on the mass of the object and the net force acting on the object.

1. A force is applied to a sled to change its motion. The mass of the sled and its cargo can be adjusted by adding or removing cargo. Complete the following graphic organizer with the terms "larger," "smaller," or "the same" for each scenario. K/U

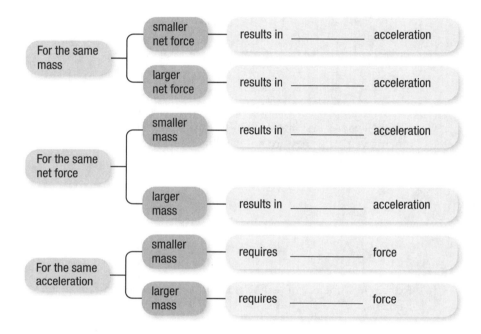

MAIN IDEA: Newton's second law states that the acceleration of any object is directly proportional to the net force acting on the object, inversely proportional to the mass of the object, and in the direction of the net force. Therefore, $\vec{a} = \dfrac{\vec{F}_{net}}{m}$.

2. If the mass of an object is quadrupled, the same net force acting on the object will produce an acceleration that is _____ times as large. K/U

3. If the net force acting on an object is quadrupled, the resulting acceleration is _____ times as large. K/U

4. The free-body diagram of a 2.2 kg object is shown below in **Figure 1**, with $\vec{F}_T = 32$ N [right] and $\vec{F}_f = 14$ N [left]. K/U

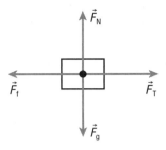

Figure 1

STUDY **TIP**

Keeping Track of Forces
In many systems, there are numerous different parts that are subjected to external applied forces and that exert forces on each other. Newton's second law relates the acceleration of any single object in the system to the sum of all the forces acting on that one object. In applying Newton's second law, always make sure you are considering only the forces acting on the object whose acceleration you are considering.

(a) Which force, or combination of forces, when divided by the mass of the object, is equal to the acceleration of the object?

(b) Determine the equation relating the acceleration of the object to its mass and the appropriate combination of forces shown.

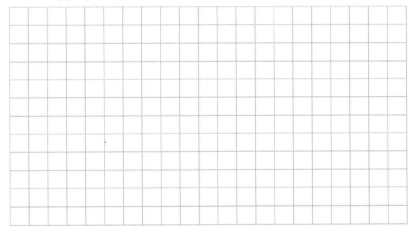

(c) Calculate the acceleration.

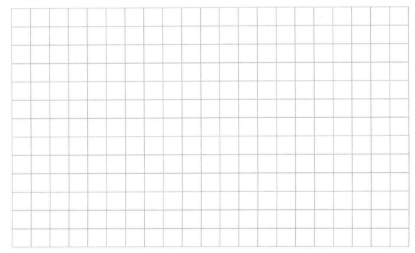

5. The acceleration of a lab cart is measured as a function of applied force, and the net force acting on the cart is calculated for each measurement. The results of this experiment are shown in the following graph (**Figure 2**). Find the mass of the lab cart from the graph, to two significant figures. T/I

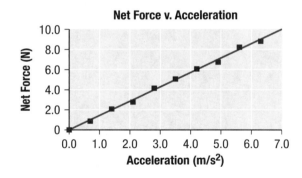

Figure 2

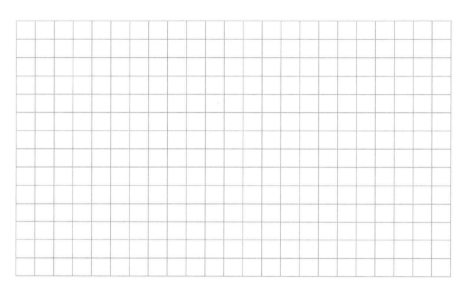

MAIN IDEA: All objects have the same acceleration $g = 9.8$ m/s^2 in free fall on Earth. Newton's law for a freely falling object is $\vec{F}_{net} = m\vec{g}$, which is usually written as $F_g = mg$ in terms of the force of gravity F_g.

6. A 0.14 kg baseball is dropped from the edge of a cliff. If air resistance can be neglected so that it is in free fall, how fast will the baseball be moving at the end of 2.2 s? T/I

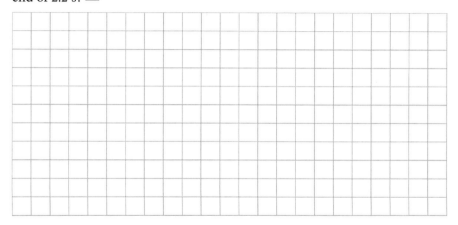

7. A heavy metal chain of mass 0.60 kg hangs over the edge of a table as shown in Figure 3. [T/I] [A]

Figure 3

(a) When half the chain is hanging over the edge, what is the magnitude of the net external force that causes the chain to accelerate?

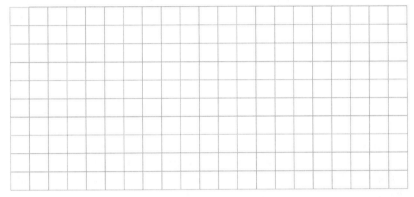

(b) Determine the acceleration of the chain when half the chain is over the edge.

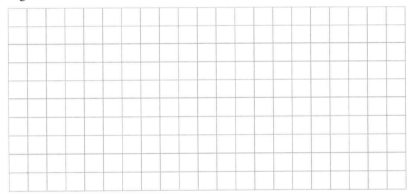

8. A rock has a mass of 2.4 kg. What is its weight in newtons on Earth? [T/I]

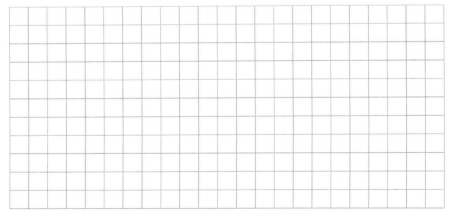

Newton's Third Law of Motion

> **Vocabulary**
>
> third law of motion

MAIN IDEA: Whenever one object exerts a force on a second object, the second object at that same instant exerts a force of the same magnitude, but in the opposite direction, on the first object. These two forces are called an action force and a reaction force. Action and reaction forces occur together simultaneously, and each is exerted on a different object in a different direction.

1. If you dive off the side of a pool into the water and consider the action force to be your feet pushing backwards and down on the edge of the pool, what is the reaction force? **K/U** **T/I**

2. Suppose you hold the end of an inflated balloon closed, and release it to allow the compressed air to be forced out the back of the balloon. Explain in terms of Newton's three laws of motion what happens to the air and the balloon before and after the balloon is released. **A**

> **STUDY TIP**
>
> **Action and Reaction**
> Although Newton introduced the terms "action" and "reaction," the terms can be misleading. The terms refer to forces, even though they sound like the names of motions; for this reason, we use "action force" and "reaction force." Also, the terms suggest that the two forces are different in some way. Actually, they are simply two forces that occur together at an instant of time and act on different objects.

3. Suppose the action force you are considering in Newton's third law is the force of pushing yourself forward to jump from a skateboard. What is the time delay between the action force and the reaction force that the skateboard exerts on you? **K/U**

4. Two students are analyzing what happens when an ice skater pushes against the boards of a skating rink. They decide that the action force and reaction force are equal in magnitude and in opposite directions, so the sum of these two forces is zero. They conclude that the skater should not move. Explain why their reasoning is incorrect. T/I

5. When you strike a nail with a hammer, the hammer stops. T/I
   (a) Did the hammer accelerate?

   (b) Was there a force acting on the hammer? How do you know this?

   (c) Explain this situation in terms of Newton's third law.

6. You and your friend are each in a canoe on a still lake. You reach out your paddle and push your friend's canoe. K/U
   (a) Which canoe accelerates from rest to begin moving?

   (b) How does the applied force on your friend's canoe compare with the force on you and your canoe?

7. A baseball collides with a bat as the batter swings and sends the ball across the field. The mass of the bat is much larger than the mass of the ball. T/I
   (a) At the moment when the baseball and the bat collide, which of them experiences the greater force?

   (b) Which one has an acceleration of the larger magnitude at that instant? Why?

Using Newton's Laws

Textbook pp. 142–147

MAIN IDEA: Newton's laws can be combined to solve problems involving forces and their effects on motion.

1. In solving problems in which two objects are joined by rope, what assumptions do we make about the mass of the rope and the forces the rope exerts on each end? K/U

2. Suppose a string joins two objects so they move together in a straight line. When calculating the acceleration of the two objects, should you consider the tension? Explain your reasoning. T/I

3. Two teams are having a tug of war. Each team exerts a force of 1500 N. What is the tension in the rope? Explain. T/I

4. An object of mass 0.60 kg hangs from a string over a pulley as shown in **Figure 1** below, with the 1.20 kg cart on the table free to accelerate without friction. Assume the 0.60 mass and the cart to be a single unit. A

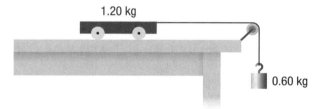

1.20 kg

0.60 kg

Figure 1

(a) What is the total mass being accelerated?

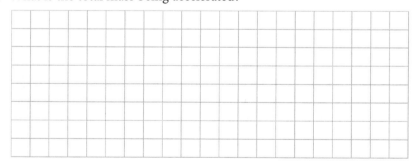

(b) What is the magnitude of the force causing the acceleration?

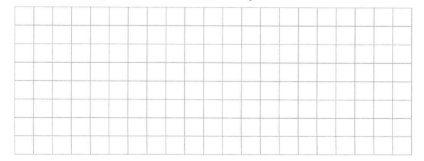

(c) Calculate the acceleration of the two objects by treating them as a single unit.

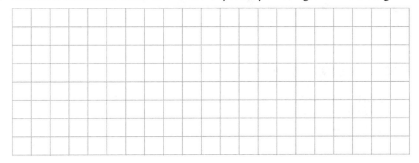

MAIN IDEA: The key equations of motion from kinematics and Newton's laws can be used together to solve motion problems.

5. What requirement must the acceleration satisfy for kinematics equations such as $\Delta d = v_i \Delta t + \frac{1}{2}a\Delta t^2$ to apply? K/U

6. What requirement must the net force on an object satisfy for the acceleration of the object to be constant? K/U

7. A 1260 kg car accelerates from rest to 27.7 m/s [forwards] in 10.0 s. T/I
   (a) Calculate the acceleration of the car.

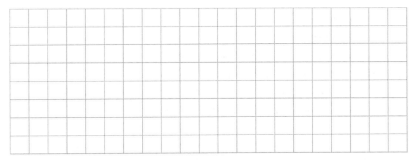

   (b) Calculate the net force acting to accelerate the car.

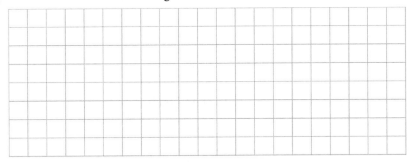

   (c) Calculate the displacement of the car during its acceleration.

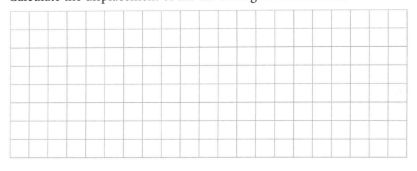

3.5 Using Newton's Laws   **53**

Textbook pp. 148–149

Galileo, Newton, and Hawking

MAIN IDEA: Newton's three laws of motion have made an impact on many other fields of science and technology, including Einstein's theory of relativity and Hawking's work on gravity and black holes.

1. What did Newton's famous book, *Principia Mathematica*, primarily focus on? K/U
   (a) forces between atoms
   (b) motion of planets
   (c) weather
   (d) rainbows

2. What was Newton's prediction about the role of the laws of physics in explaining other phenomena that were not well understood at that time, such as light? K/U

3. Earth's gravity exerts a force of gravity on a satellite in orbit around it. Which of these is true? A
   (a) The satellite exerts a much smaller gravity force on Earth.
   (b) The satellite exerts an equally strong force on Earth.
   (c) Newton's laws do not apply to action-at-a-distance forces like gravity.
   (d) Gravity does not apply if an object is in orbit.

4. What did Einstein's work on special relativity deal with? How did this differ from what his theory of general relativity deals with? K/U

5. A black hole is an astronomical body of such huge mass that nothing, not even light, was believed to be able to escape from its gravity. How is this view different from the most current view of black holes? K/U

6. Newton said he had "stood on the shoulders of giants." What was he referring to? K/U

Newton's Laws of Motion

Use the graphic organizer below to summarize what you have learned about Newton's laws of motion. You can add your own notes, diagrams, and equations to this graphic organizer, creating a study tool to help you review Chapter 3.

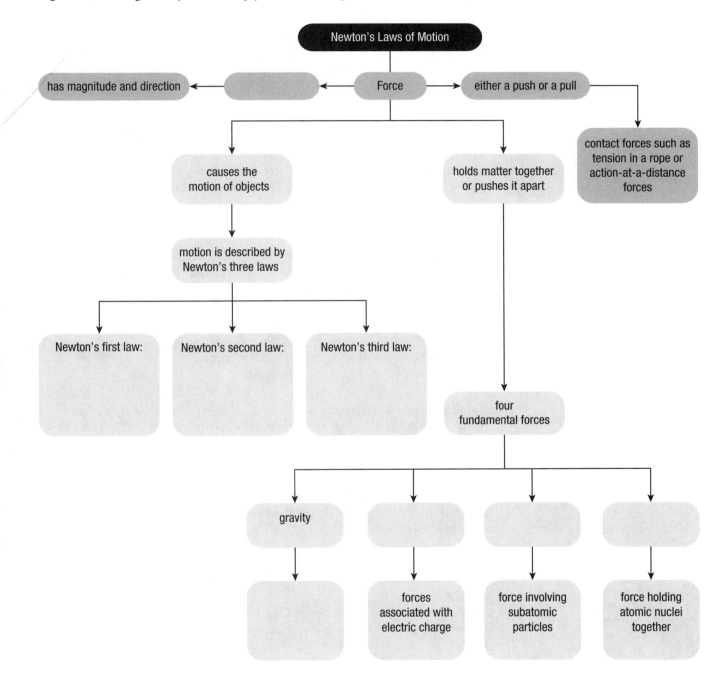

K/U Knowledge/Understanding
T/I Thinking/Investigation
C   Communication
A   Application

1. Complete **Table 1**. (3.1) K/U

Table 1 Action-at-a-Distance and Contact Forces

Force	Action at a distance or contact?
force exerted by a rope	
gravity	
one electric charge attracting another	
one magnet repelling another 0.5 cm away	
force of pushing a car	

2. Is the following statement true or false? If you think the statement is false, rewrite it to make it true: Newton's second law states that if the mass of an object is twice as great for the same force, then the acceleration that results is twice as great. (3.3) K/U

3. You push on a frictionless cart with a force of 20 N. According to Newton's third law, there is a reaction force of equal magnitude in the opposite direction, yet the net force is not zero and the cart accelerates. Why is this the case? (3.4) K/U
   (a) The applied force, not the net force, determines acceleration.
   (b) The action and reaction forces act on different objects.
   (c) The action force overcomes the reaction force.
   (d) The acceleration depends on the mass.

4. Describe how to calculate the net force on an object when several different forces, each with a different magnitude and direction, act on the object. (3.1) K/U

5. (a) When you apply Newton's second law $F_{net} = ma$ to the weight of an object, which variable describing the effect of gravity corresponds to F, and which to a?

   (b) What is the resulting relationship between mass and weight?

   (c) Suppose you took a hammer of known mass to the Moon and weighed it. How could the weight you measured and the known mass of the hammer be used to calculate the effect of gravity on the hammer or any other object on the Moon? Write the equation you would use and explain what you could calculate from it. (3.3) K/U T/I

6. Suppose you are pushing a cart filled with groceries with a force of 30 N to keep it at constant velocity. What net force is acting on the cart? How is that possible when you are exerting a significant applied force? (3.2) T/I

7. If the force of a collision brings a car to a sudden stop, the passengers feel themselves thrown forward rather than feeling themselves pushed backwards from the force of the collision. Explain why this happens. (3.2) K/U

8. Three carts are linked together as shown in **Figure 1**. The mass of each cart is $m_1 = 2$. A force of 12 N pulls the cart on the right. Calculate the force acting on the last cart (on the left). (3.5) T/I

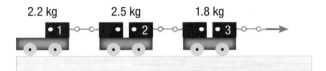

Figure 1

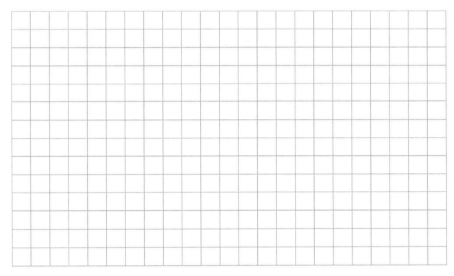

9. Explain why the winning team in a tug of war is the one that exerts the stronger net force on the ground, but not on their end of the rope. (3.5) A

10. Did people have to know Newton's laws to invent and use devices in which forces control motion? Choose a familiar device as an example, and justify your reasoning about whether it was necessary to know Newton's laws to design and operate it. (3.6) T/I

Gravitational Force Near Earth

> **Vocabulary**
>
> free fall   terminal speed   force field   gravitational field strength

MAIN IDEA: Gravity is the force that attracts objects to Earth.

1. When is an object in free fall? **K/U**

STUDY TIP

Making a List
As you read about a new physical quantity like Earth's gravitational field, you can make a list of its important properties.

---

2. A baseball is released from a balloon at a height of 50 m. **K/U**
   (a) How does the air resistance acting on the baseball vary with the velocity of the baseball?

   (b) What are the initial velocity and acceleration of the baseball?

   (c) What is the magnitude of the air resistance just after the baseball is released?

   (d) How does the speed change as the baseball falls?

   (e) How does the air resistance change as the baseball falls?

   (f) How does the acceleration of the baseball change as it falls?

3. Complete **Table 1** below with the words "increased," "decreased," or "unchanged." **K/U**

   Table 1 Factors That Affect Air Resistance of a Falling Object

	If the object has	Then the force of air resistance is
(a)	a larger cross-sectional area	
(b)	greater mass	
(c)	greater speed	

4. A skydiver jumps from a plane and soon is falling downward at constant speed. **T/I** **C**

(a) Draw the free-body diagram of the skydiver at constant speed.

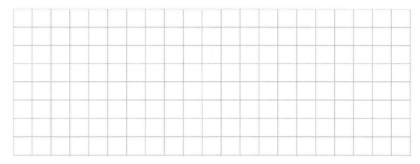

(b) Identify the forces acting on the skydiver.

(c) Describe how the magnitudes and directions of the forces acting on the skydiver are related.

STUDY **TIP**

Apparent Weightlessness
Inside a falling elevator, you and your surroundings would fall at the same rate, and you would feel the same apparent weightlessness experienced by astronauts in orbit. If the elevator is merely accelerating downward when it first begins to move, you experience only a decrease in apparent weight, and a scale you stand on inside the elevator would display a smaller than normal weight during the brief acceleration.

MAIN IDEA: Gravity is an action-at-a-distance force between any two objects. The force of gravity that the Earth exerts on any other object is described by Earth's gravitational field.

5. Earth is surrounded by a gravitational force field. What effect does the field have on any object placed in it? **K/U**

6. Complete **Table 2** below with properties of Earth's gravitational field. **K/U**

Table 2 Properties of Earth's Gravitational Field

	Field property	Description
(a)	direction of Earth's gravitational field	
(b)	magnitude of the field at Earth's surface (with units)	
(c)	effect of increased distance from Earth's centre on the magnitude of the field	
(d)	expression for the magnitude of the force on an object of mass m in the field $\vec{g}$	

7. Compare and contrast mass and weight in each of the following respects. K/U
   (a) the meaning of "mass" versus the meaning of "weight"

   (b) how the mass and weight of an object would be affected if placed on a planet other than Earth

   (c) the SI units of mass versus the SI units of weight

8. The force of gravity is much weaker on the Moon than on Earth. Suppose you pitched a baseball on the Moon by applying exactly the same force in the same way as on Earth. T/I
   (a) How would the velocity of the baseball pitched on the Moon compare with the velocity for the same pitch on Earth? Explain your reasoning.

   (b) If you pitched the baseball straight upward in the same way on Earth and on the Moon, how would the height reached by the ball compare? Explain.

9. A package is suspended from a spring scale that reads 35 N. Determine the mass of the package. T/I

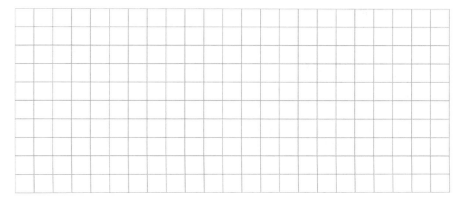

Friction

Textbook pp. 168–172

Vocabulary

static friction ($\vec{F}_s$)   coefficient of friction (μ)   coefficient of kinetic friction (μ_K)

kinetic friction ($\vec{F}_k$)   coefficient of static friction (μ_S)

MAIN IDEA: Friction occurs both between two surfaces at rest relative to each other, and between two surfaces moving past each other.

1. How does static friction differ from kinetic friction? K/U

2. A heavy crate is at rest on the ground while a worker pushes it with gradually increasing force. The crate does not move when the force is still weak because
    (a) the applied force is not large enough to overcome inertia
    (b) the force of static friction cancels the applied force
    (c) the force of static friction exceeds the applied force
    (d) the force of kinetic friction prevents motion K/U

3. A heavy crate rests on the ground and does not move as a worker increases the force applied. Does the increase in applied force cause the friction force to increase, decrease, or remain unchanged? K/U

4. At what point does a crate resting on the ground begin to move in response to the applied force? K/U

> **STUDY TIP**
>
> **Sketch a Diagram**
> In any problem that involves combining friction forces with other forces, you can visualize the relations between relative directions and magnitudes of all the forces by sketching a free-body diagram, even if none is requested.

5. A grocery cart is pushed at constant speed. Friction in the wheel bearings acts to oppose its motion. To keep the grocery cart moving at constant speed,
    (a) the applied force must be zero
    (b) the applied force must exceed the force of friction
    (c) the applied force must have the same direction and magnitude as friction
    (d) the applied force and friction force must cancel each other K/U

6. Complete **Table 1** below to describe different types of friction. K/U

    Table 1 Some Types of Friction

	Example	Type of kinetic friction
(a)	resistance to the motion of a sled along level snow	
(b)	resistance to the turning motion of a wheel along the ground	
(c)	resistance to the motion of a ship moving through water	

MAIN IDEA: For an object in contact with a horizontal surface, the maximum force of static friction, and the force of kinetic friction, each are directly proportional to the normal force between the two surfaces. The proportionality constants in these two relations depend on the materials in contact and on the characteristics of their surfaces.

7. How does the coefficient of static friction usually compare in magnitude with the coefficient of kinetic friction? **K/U**

8. A sled is being pulled along level ground at constant speed by a dog team. If the load carried by the sled is increased, how does this affect the force that the dog team must exert to maintain the constant speed of the sled? Explain your reasoning. **A**

9. A 0.90 kg textbook is pushed forward along a table at a constant velocity by a force of 1.3 N. **T/I**
   (a) Determine the weight of the book.

   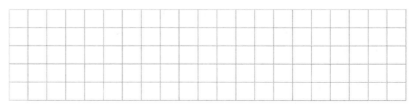

   (b) Determine the magnitude of the normal force.

   (c) Determine the magnitude of the friction force.

   (d) Determine the coefficient of kinetic friction.

   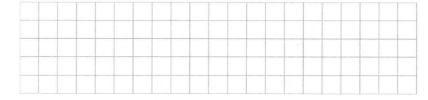

10. A 0.90 kg textbook rests on a desk. The horizontal applied force acting on it is slowly increased. The coefficient of static friction between the book and desk surface is 0.18. Find the smallest applied force that will cause the book to start moving. **T/I**

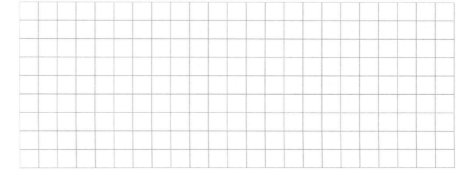

Solving Friction Problems

MAIN IDEA: Static friction problems involve objects being kept at rest by friction despite an applied force. Static friction can be used to cause motion by holding one object in place while it exerts a force on another object that is free to move.

Textbook pp. 173–178

1. A horizontal rope pulls five skiers across the snow. Each has a mass of 75 kg. The coefficient of static friction of the waxed skis on snow is 0.10. Assuming the skiers are initially at rest, find the applied force needed to start the motion of the five skiers. **T/I**

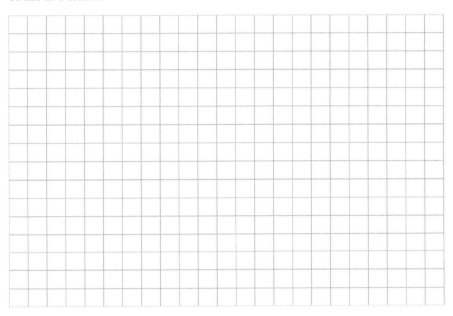

> ### STUDY TIP
>
> **Concept Maps**
> You can construct a concept map to organize how the key ideas of a chapter are organized. You can also preview the concept map in this Study Guide to get an overview of the key topics in the chapter before studying it.

2. What determines the maximum force a runner can exert without his shoes slipping on the ground to accelerate forward? **K/U**

3. A runner is competing in a marathon. She has gained 1.3 times her mass since last year's race. **T/I**
   (a) How will the difference in mass affect the runner's weight, the runner's normal force, and the maximum force of static friction of the runner's shoes on the ground?

   (b) How will increasing the mass by a factor of 1.3 affect the force that the runner can exert to accelerate without slipping?

(c) Given how increasing the mass by a factor of 1.3 affects the maximum force the runner can exert to accelerate, and how the greater mass affects the acceleration for any given force, how does the increase of mass by a factor of 1.3 affect the acceleration that the runner can achieve without sliding on the track surface? Explain your reasoning.

4. A rope is attached to a sled on a level ice surface. Someone standing on an asphalt surface near the ice pulls the rope. The person pulling the rope has a mass of 72 kg and is wearing shoes whose soles have a coefficient of static friction of 0.70 on asphalt. The mass of the sled and its passenger is 120 kg.

(a) How hard can the person on the asphalt surface pull the rope without slipping?

(b) What maximum acceleration of the sled does this produce?

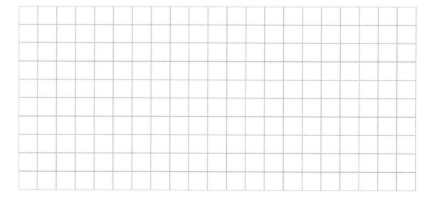

MAIN IDEA: Kinetic friction acts on a moving object in a direction opposite to its motion. Newton's laws and the kinematic equations can be used to solve problems involving kinetic friction.

5. What is the direction of kinetic friction relative to the velocity? K/U

6. What direction must an applied force have relative to the velocity for the applied force to be in the same direction as kinetic friction? K/U

7. A 1300 kg car is travelling at 16 m/s with an air resistance force of $\vec{F}_K = 340$ N when its brakes are applied to produce an additional force $\vec{F}_a$ to slow the car. Other forces acting on the car are the weight of the car $\vec{F}_g$, and the normal force $\vec{F}_N$. T/I C

   (a) Draw the free-body diagram of the car. Mark the direction of motion relative to the force vectors in the diagram.

   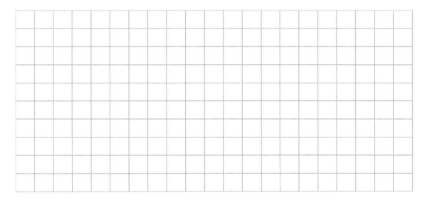

   (b) How large is the force $\vec{F}_a$ applied by the brakes if it slows the car from 16 m/s to 14 m/s in 2.0 s?

   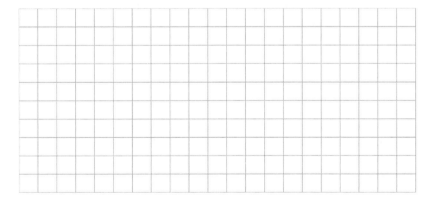

Forces Applied to Automotive Technology

MAIN IDEA: Car tires are kept from skidding by static friction, which is maximized for rubber tires when the tire surface area in contact with the road increases.

1. Is the following statement true or false? If you think the statement is false, rewrite it to make it true: In most cases, the maximum force of static friction depends on the amount of surface area in contact between the two surfaces. K/U

2. When a car is driven along the road, _____ friction keeps the tires from slipping on the road surface. K/U

3. Explain the purpose of the grooves in a tire used on a passenger car. K/U

STUDY **TIP**

Highlighting Key Points
As you read through the Study Guide, underline or highlight the answers that summarize points in the chapter that you want to review further in the textbook or discuss with others.

4. (a) What is hydroplaning?

   (b) Why is hydroplaning dangerous?

   (c) Sipes are valleys that run across the bottom of the tire, usually perpendicular to the grooves. How can sipes provide additional protection against hydroplaning? K/U

5. What driving practices reduce the likelihood of hydroplaning? K/U

6. When the tread on a tire has worn out so that the tire is bald, the tire will have (high/low) _____ friction on a dry road and (high/low) _____ friction on a wet road. K/U

7. Why is it dangerous to lock the brakes while bringing a car to an emergency stop? K/U

8. How does an anti-lock braking system work to allow the brakes to stop the car without skidding? K/U

9. How does traction control in a passenger vehicle help prevent the tires from sliding while increasing speed? K/U

10. Using your knowledge of forces, explain how a car with a crumple zone that collapses in a collision provides better passenger protection than a car whose front half is solidly designed so that it remains relatively rigid in a collision. T/I A

11. How does an airbag reduce injuries in a collision? K/U

12. What dangers do airbags pose? K/U

4.5

Forces Applied to Sports and Research

MAIN IDEA: The study of forces has numerous applications in improving sports technology.

1. What is the advantage of striking a golf ball using the centre of a golf club's head? K/U

2. A golfer typically chooses which club to use depending on conditions. Fill in **Table 1** below listing how different characteristics of the golf club make it more suitable for the specific need. K/U

   Table 1 Golf Club Characteristics

	Specific need	Characteristic of the golf club
(a)	increase maximum force of static friction with the player's hands	The grip of the club is made of _____.
(b)	club designed for long-distance shot	The shaft should be (longer/shorter) _____ so that the head moves (faster/slower) _____
(c)	less tendency for the head of the club to twist while striking the ball	The head should be made (heavier/ lighter) _____.

3. List an example of sports footwear that requires a low coefficient of friction between the footwear and the ground, and an example that requires a high coefficient of friction. K/U

   low friction example: _____

   high friction example: _____

4. What produces the extremely low coefficient of friction of ice under an ice skate? K/U

   (a) Ice is melted by thermal energy from friction.
   (b) Ice is melted by the pressure from the ice skate blades.
   (c) A thin surface layer of melted ice is already present except at extremely low temperatures.
   (d) Ice is melted because of the warmth of the ice skate blades.

5. What feature of the blade design allows a skater to exert a force on the ice needed to accelerate, despite the low coefficient of static friction? K/U

6. When a runner steps downward to change direction, the base of the runner's foot must exert a force for a short time on the base of the shoe to reverse the runner's direction. How does the use of a foam insole reduce the normal force on a runner's foot required to do this? A

7. Describe how a rolling element bearing differs from a plain bearing. K/U

8. What is a prosthesis? Give at least three common examples. K/U

9. What are some of the features an artificial limb should have to make it as useful as possible? K/U

10. Carbon has been found to form into arrangements of carbon atoms that can provide a surface with very low friction. What are some of the uses that a coating of this kind might potentially have? K/U

Textbook pp. 189–190

Mandatory Snow Tires in the Winter?

MAIN IDEA: Snow tires make driving safer during the winter months because of their greater traction than other tires on snow and ice. They are less suitable for summer driving. Many people believe that all drivers should be required to use snow tires on their cars during winter months. Others consider all-season radials good enough or believe individual drivers should make their own decision without a mandatory snow tire law.

1. What differences in the construction of snow tires make them better for driving on snow-covered roads? (Hint: See the photos on page 189 of the textbook.) T/I A

2. List at least two disadvantages of switching to snow tires each winter. K/U

3. Many people feel they should decide for themselves whether to mount snow tires on their car each winter. List at least two considerations that argue for voluntary compliance, and two that argue in favour of mandatory compliance. K/U

4. Would you recommend mandatory snow tire laws for your community? Explain. C

Applications of Forces

Fill in the blanks in the graphic organizer below to summarize the main ideas from Chapter 4.

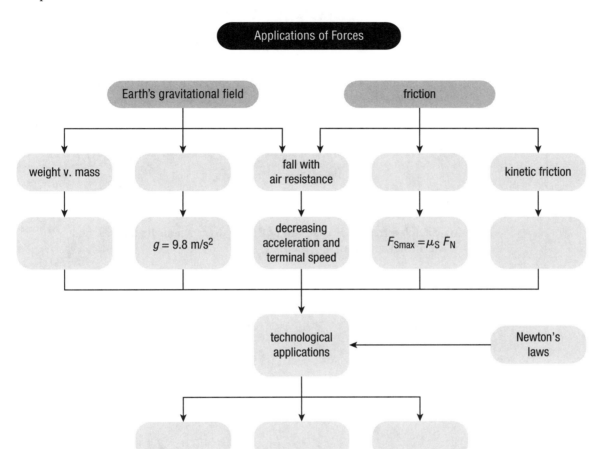

K/U Knowledge/Understanding
T/I Thinking/Investigation
C Communication
A Application

1. Earth's gravity inside the International Space station is
   (a) zero
   (b) the same as on Earth's surface
   (c) weaker than on Earth's surface but still substantial
   (d) extremely small but not zero, hence the name "microgravity" (4.1) K/U

2. A skydiver jumps from a plane. (4.1) K/U C
   (a) Sketch a free-body diagram of the skydiver immediately after stepping out of the plane.

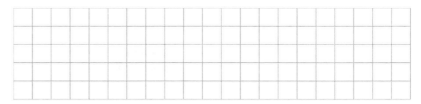

   (b) Sketch a free-body diagram of the skydiver when she has reached terminal speed.

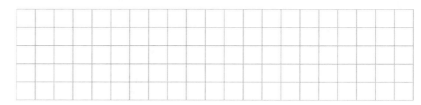

   (c) Describe how the air resistance force changes as time passes from the jump to reaching terminal speed.

   (d) How does the air resistance force produced by the skydiver compare with the air resistance force produced at the same speed of fall by having a parachute open? Explain your reasoning.

3. Complete **Table 1** below. (4.1) K/U

   Table 1 Properties of Mass and Weight

	What about an object does it directly measure?	Does it change with location?	Name of SI unit	SI unit in terms of kg, m, and s
Mass			kilogram	
Weight			newton	

4. How does static friction differ from kinetic friction? (4.2) K/U

5. When you apply a force to try to move a desk along the floor, and then push harder without success, the force of static friction opposing your effort (increases/decreases/stays the same) _____. (4.2) K/U

6. What determines the direction of the force of kinetic friction? (4.3) K/U

7. (a) What kind of friction is used in brakes to produce the force that the brakes exert on the wheels? _____
   (b) What kind of friction acts between the tires and the road to exert the force that stops the car? _____ (4.4) K/U

8. How do seat belts enhance safety? (4.4) K/U

9. How does a rolling element bearing differ from a typical fluid bearing? (4.5) K/U

10. If you fired a cannonball on Earth, and then fired an identical cannonball from an identical cannon on the Moon where gravity is much weaker, would the cannonball leave the cannon faster, more slowly, or at the same speed on the Moon? Explain your reasoning. (4.1) T/I

11. You want to move a 40.0 kg desk to a different corner of your room. Its coefficient of static friction with the floor is 0.30 and its coefficient of kinetic friction is 0.25. (4.2) T/I
    (a) How much force must you exert on the desk to make it slide along the floor?

    (b) How much force must you continue to exert to move the desk at constant velocity to its destination?

K/U Knowledge/Understanding
T/I Thinking/Investigation
C   Communication
A   Application

1. Tires are designed with grooves in their tread in order to
   (a) allow water under the tire to escape
   (b) increase the normal force of the tire on the road
   (c) help cool the tire
   (d) allow air to flow under the tire (4.4) K/U

2. A hockey puck on a layer of ice is initially at rest, and then is pushed by a hockey stick. Complete **Table 1** to describe how each of Newton's laws applies. (3.2–3.4) K/U

   Table 1 Newton's Three Laws

	Newton's law	Statement of the law	How the law applies
(a)	first law	If the net force on an object is _____ then the acceleration it produces is _____	
(b)	second law	The acceleration of an object is _____ proportional to the net force on it and _____ proportional to its _____.	The hockey puck accelerates when it is pushed.
(c)	third law	The force that one object exerts on a second object has the same _____ and opposite _____ as the force that the second object exerts on the first object.	

3. When you pitch a baseball and exert a force on it, there is also a reaction force. Fill in **Table 2** listing the characteristics of the reaction force for a thrown baseball. (3.4) K/U

   Table 2 Action and Reaction Forces

(a)	magnitude of the reaction force compared to the force you exert on the baseball	
(b)	relative directions of the action and reaction forces	
(c)	object the reaction force acts on	
(d)	When does the reaction force act relative to the action force?	
(e)	Is the reaction force included in the net force on the baseball?	

4. Four blocks of wood, each with a mass of $m = 1.2$ kg, are attached by strings as shown in **Figure 1**. The tension in the first string, connected to block 1, is 11.2 N. The coefficient of kinetic friction for each block is $\mu_K = 0.22$. (3.1, 3.5, 4.2, 4.3) K/U C

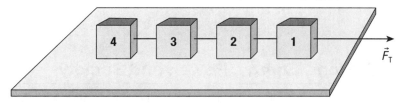

Figure 1

(a) Draw a free-body diagram for the forces acting on block number 4, including the normal force $\vec{F}_N$, gravitational force $\vec{F}_g$, applied force $\vec{F}_{T,4}$ from the string, and friction force $\vec{F}_f$.

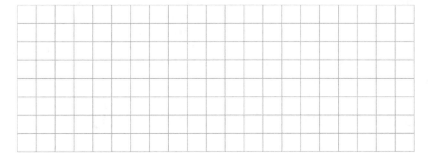

(b) Determine the total friction force on the four blocks.

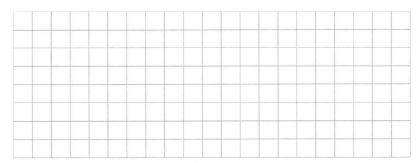

5. To judge which of two objects is more massive, you could hold one in each hand and move them up and down together to compare the resistance each offers to the force you exert. Would this method work under conditions of zero or negligible gravity? Explain your reasoning. (4.1) T/I

6. Race cars are often built with a spoiler—a wing-like structure that deflects air upward—on the rear of the car. Explain in terms of Newton's laws how the spoiler affects the normal force between the race car's rear tires and the ground. Then explain in terms of the concepts of this unit what effect this has on friction between the tires and the road. (4.2–4.4) T/I

Energy and Society

BIG IDEAS

- Energy can be transformed from one type into another.
- Energy transformation systems often involve thermal energy losses and are never 100 % efficient.
- Although technological applications that involve energy transformations can affect society and the environment in positive ways, they can also have negative effects, and therefore must be used responsibly.

Chapter 5: Work, Energy, Power, and Society

Work, energy, and power are related concepts that affect everyday life, society, and the environment. In science, energy is defined as the capacity to do work, which occurs when a force displaces an object. There are many types of energy, such as thermal energy and sound energy. All types of energy fall under the categories of potential energy, kinetic energy, or a combination of both.

According to the law of conservation of energy, the total amount of energy in the universe does not change. Energy cannot be created nor destroyed, but it can be transformed, or changed from one form to another.

Power is the rate at which energy is transformed or work is done; efficiency quantifies the amount of useful energy produced when energy is transformed. The selection and use of energy resources, some renewable and others non-renewable, impact society and the environment.

Chapter 6: Thermal Energy and Society

Thermal energy, temperature, and heat are similar concepts, but these terms are not interchangeable. Thermal energy is the total amount of potential and kinetic energy possessed by the particles of a substance. Temperature is the average kinetic energy of the particles. Heat is the term used to describe the transfer of thermal energy. Change in the thermal energy of a substance can cause changes of state, such as melting or freezing.

Heating and cooling systems, which keep homes, schools, and businesses comfortable, are familiar applications of the concepts of thermal energy, temperature, and heat. These systems can have both positive and negative impacts on the environment.

Chapter 7: Nuclear Energy and Society

Nuclear energy is released during changes in the structure of atomic nuclei. Some forms of atoms, called isotopes, change spontaneously, releasing energy called radiation. This process has practical applications, such as carbon-14 dating and medical diagnosis. There are several different types of radioactive decay reactions, each with different characteristics.

Very large amounts of energy are released in fission reactions, and this makes nuclear fission a useful energy source. However, there are safety and waste disposal issues related to the use of nuclear fission as a power source.

Nuclear fusion, which is the source of the Sun's energy as well as the energy of all other stars, is a reaction in which the nuclei of two atoms fuse and a great amount of energy is released. Nuclear fusion is better than nuclear fission from an environmental standpoint, but it is very difficult to achieve. At present, nuclear fusion is not a practical source of energy.

Work

Textbook pp. 222–229

Vocabulary
mechanical work *(W)*

MAIN IDEA: Mechanical work is done when a force displaces an object in the direction of the force or a component of the force.

1. What equation can be used to calculate work when the magnitude of the force is constant and the force and displacement are in the same direction? K/U

2. The SI unit for work is the _____, also called the
_____. K/U

3. Identify a task that is considered work in the everyday sense, but not in the scientific sense. Explain why this task is not considered work in the scientific sense. K/U A

> **LEARNING TIP**
>
> **Describing Work**
> When describing work, you should always mention the object that does the work and the object that the work is done on.

> **LEARNING TIP**
>
> **Work**
> Work has a different meaning in science than it does in everyday life. In science, work is done only when a force displaces an object. If a force is applied to an object, but the object does not move, then no work is done.

4. A student applies a force of 25.0 N to a classroom desk, resulting in the desk moving 5.50 m in the direction the force was applied. How much mechanical work did the student do on the desk? Show your calculations below. T/I

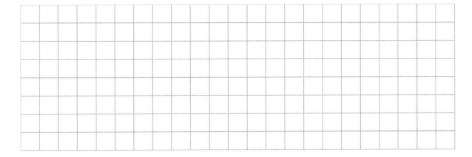

MAIN IDEA: The equation $W = F(\cos\theta)\Delta d$ may be used to calculate the amount of mechanical work done on an object.

5. Fill in **Table 1** below to show the relationship between the direction of the force, the direction of the displacement, and the work done. K/U

Table 1 Force, Displacement, and Work

Relationship of force to displacement	θ	$\cos\theta$	Work done (positive, negative, or no work done)
same direction			
perpendicular			
opposite directions			

6. A person pushes snow across a flat driveway using a snow shovel. The force exerted on the snow shovel by the person is 92 N at an angle of 30.0° with the driveway. The snow shovel moves 1.5 m across the driveway. How much mechanical work is done on the snow shovel? Show your calculations below. **T/I**

MAIN IDEA: When the force on an object and the displacement of the object are parallel (in the same direction or opposite in direction), the work done on the object may be determined from an *F–d* graph by finding the area between the graph and the positive axis. The work is positive if the area is above the position axis and negative if it is below the position axis.

7. Which section or sections of the graph shown in **Figure 1** below represent positive work? How do you know? **K/U**

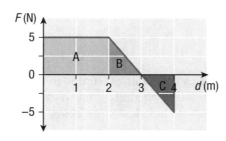

Figure 1

MAIN IDEA: When a force varies in magnitude during a displacement, the work done is equal to the product of the average force, F_{av}, and the displacement, Δd.

8. A force of varying magnitude is applied to a table that is being pushed horizontally across the floor. The displacement is 27 m and the average force applied is 13.5 N. What is the total work done on the table? Show your calculations. **T/I**

9. Is the work you calculated for question 8 positive or negative? Explain. K/U

10. In the space below, draw an *F–d* graph that illustrates the information given in question 8. Assume that the force increases from 0 N to 27 N at a constant rate. T/I

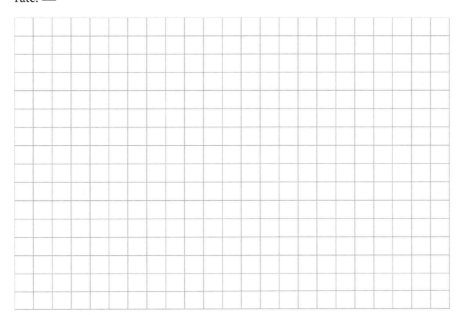

Energy

Textbook pp. 230–235

Vocabulary

energy

kinetic energy (E_k)

work–energy principle

potential energy

gravitational potential energy

reference level

mechanical energy

MAIN IDEA: Energy is the capacity (ability) to do work.

1. Energy can be categorized as _____ energy, which is the energy of moving objects, and _____ energy, which is stored energy that an object possesses due to its position in relation to forces in its environment. **K/U**

MAIN IDEA: The kinetic energy of an object with mass, m, and speed, v, is given by $E_k = \dfrac{mv^2}{2}$.

2. Calculate the kinetic energy of a 220 g snowball that is moving at a constant speed of 5.0 m/s. Show your work below. **T/I**

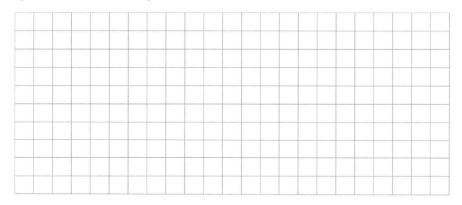

3. A car and a large truck travel side by side on a highway for a 5.0 km distance at a speed of 100.0 km/h. Explain why these two vehicles, which have the same velocity, have different amounts of kinetic energy. **T/I** **A**

MAIN IDEA: The total work, W_{net}, done on an object results in a change in the object's kinetic energy: $W_{net} = E_{kf} - E_{ki}$, where E_{kf} and E_{ki} represent the final and initial kinetic energy of the object respectively. In other words, $W_{net} = \Delta E_k$.

4. Restate the work–energy principle in your own words. **K/U** **C**

5. A truck with a mass of 2355 kg starts from rest and accelerates to a speed of 23 m/s over 65 m. Calculate the net work done on the truck. K/U

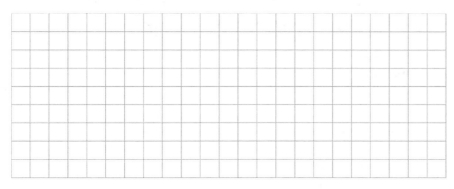

MAIN IDEA: Gravitational potential energy is possessed by an object based on its position relative to a reference level, which is often the ground. $E_g = mgh$ where h is the height above the chosen reference level.

6. Define the term *reference level*. K/U

7. What is an object's gravitational potential energy value when it is at the reference level? K/U

8. Fill in **Table 1** below to explain what is indicated by each part of the equation $E_g = mgh$. K/U

Table 1 Variables for Gravitational Potential Energy

Variable	Meaning
E_g	gravitational potential energy of object
m	
g	
h	

MAIN IDEA: Mechanical energy is the sum of kinetic energy and gravitational potential energy.

9. At a given moment, a pencil falling to the floor has 8 J of kinetic energy and 19 J of gravitational potential energy. What is the mechanical energy of the pencil? T/I

10. Describe how the gravitational potential energy and kinetic energy of a raindrop change as it falls to the ground from a cloud. Then describe the mechanical energy of the raindrop during the same time period. T/I C

Types of Energy and the Law of Conservation of Energy

Vocabulary

thermal energy

nuclear energy

energy transformation

law of conservation of energy

MAIN IDEA: Energy exists in many forms.

1. Fill in the concept map below to describe some types of energy. K/U

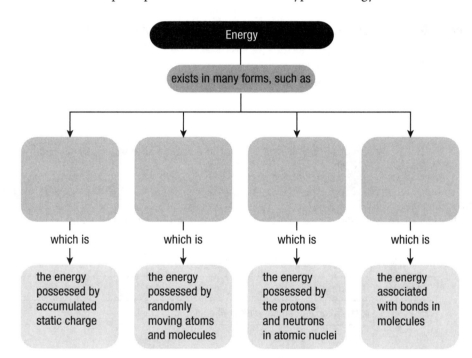

Energy

exists in many forms, such as

which is | which is | which is | which is

the energy possessed by accumulated static charge

the energy possessed by randomly moving atoms and molecules

the energy possessed by the protons and neutrons in atomic nuclei

the energy associated with bonds in molecules

MAIN IDEA: In an energy transformation, energy changes from one form into another.

2. Describe an energy transformation, other than photosynthesis, that occurs in a natural system. K/U

3. Describe an energy transformation that occurs in a technological system other than a light bulb or internal combustion engine. K/U T/I

MAIN IDEA: The law of conservation of energy states that when energy is changed from one form into another, no energy is lost.

4. Use the words in the word bank to complete the paragraph below. K/U

changed	created	form	universe
conserved	energy	lost	disappear

_____ in the universe is _____. There is a certain total amount of energy in the _____, and this total never changes. When an energy transformation occurs, no energy is _____, new energy cannot be _____ out of nothing, and existing energy cannot _____. The energy that exists can only be _____ from one _____ into another.

MAIN IDEA: When using the law of conservation of energy to solve problems, you may find the total mechanical energy, E_m, at one point in the motion of the object and then equate it to the total mechanical energy at another point. The total mechanical energy is $E_m = E_g + E_k$.

5. Complete the flow chart below to describe the changes in energy that occur when a squirrel holds an acorn with a mass of 0.020 kg on a tree branch 5.0 m above the ground, and then drops the acorn through the air to the ground. Use the space below the flow chart for your calculations. T/I

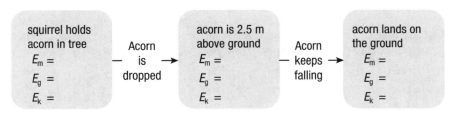

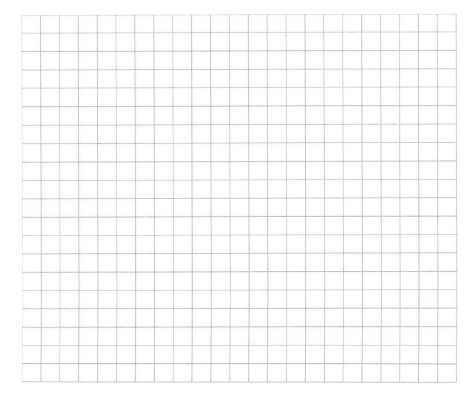

Efficiency, Energy Sources, and Energy Conservation

Vocabulary

efficiency	fossil fuel	passive solar design
energy resource	nuclear fission	photovoltaic cell
non-renewable energy resource	nuclear fusion	hydroelectricity
renewable energy resource	solar energy	

MAIN IDEA: The equation to calculate the efficiency of an energy transformation is $\dfrac{E_{out}}{E_{in}} \times 100\ \%$, where E_{out} is the useful energy output and E_{in} is the energy input.

1. State the definition of the term *efficiency* in your own words. K/U C

2. Calculate the efficiency of an electric heater if 4.0×10^2 J of electrical energy produces 384 J of heat energy. Show your work. T/I A

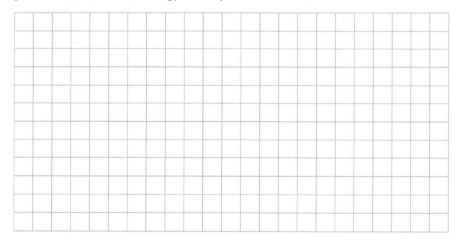

MAIN IDEA: No energy-transforming device is 100 % efficient. Typically the waste energy is in the form of thermal energy.

3. Many people have replaced incandescent light bulbs with compact fluorescent bulbs, because compact fluorescent bulbs are more efficient. Use this information to determine which type of bulb becomes hotter during use, and explain your response. T/I A

MAIN IDEA: Non-renewable energy resources are energy-rich substances that cannot be replenished when they are used up in the energy transformation process.

4. List three common fossil fuels. K/U

5. Summarize how fossil fuels are formed. K/U C

MAIN IDEA: Renewable energy resources are energy-rich substances with an unlimited supply or a supply that can be replenished.

6. Complete **Table 1** to compare renewable energy resources. K/U

Table 1 Energy Resources

Energy source	Energy transformation	Drawbacks or concerns
solar		
tidal		
wind		

STUDY TIP

Using Tables
Use tables to summarize information. On a separate sheet of paper, expand this table to include information about other energy sources.

MAIN IDEA: There are many ways to conserve energy.

7. Read the list of tips for conserving energy on page 249 in the textbook. Then, write a paragraph identifying two tips that you feel you could incorporate into your everyday life, and describe how you could incorporate those tips. C A

LEARNING TIP

"Conserving Energy" and "the Law of Conservation of Energy"
When we say "conserve energy" or "energy conservation," we are referring to ways in which people may avoid wasting energy. However, the law of conservation of energy refers to the idea that the total amount of energy is conserved when one form of energy is transformed into another form of energy.

Power

Textbook pp. 250–254

Vocabulary

power (P)

Power and the Work–Energy Principle
Although we developed the work–energy principle ($W_{net} = \Delta E$) in terms of changes in an object's kinetic energy, the principle also applies when an object's potential energy changes.

MAIN IDEA: Power is the rate of transforming energy or the rate of doing work. The equations for power are $P = \dfrac{W_{net}}{\Delta t}$ or $P = \dfrac{\Delta E}{\Delta t}$.

1. Use words to summarize the equation $P = \dfrac{\Delta E}{\Delta t}$. **K/U**

2. A baseball bat does 120 J of work on a baseball in 0.4 s. What is the baseball bat's power? Show your work below. **T/I**

Restating Equations
Restating mathematical equations as words can help you clarify the meaning of the equation.

3. By examining the equations used to calculate power, what can you determine about the relationship between W_{net} and ΔE? **T/I**

MAIN IDEA: Power is a scalar quantity measured in watts (1 W = 1 J/s).

4. Why is power a scalar quantity? **K/U**

5. The unit watt is named after _____ _____, an engineer who invented the first practical _____. **K/U**

MAIN IDEA: Electrical devices transform electrical energy into other forms of energy, and the power rating of these devices can be determined using the equations for power.

6. Which device in **Table 1** transforms electrical energy at the greatest rate? Explain your reasoning.

Table 1 Power Ratings

Appliance	Power rating (W)
laptop computer	20–75
vacuum cleaner	200–700
microwave oven	600–1500
dishwasher	1200–1500
refrigerator	100–500
stove	6000–10 000

MAIN IDEA: The electrical energy used by an electrical device can be found using the equation $\Delta E = P\Delta t$.

7. If a microwave oven with a power rating of 850 W runs for 62 s, how much electrical energy does it use in that time? Show your work below. **T/I**

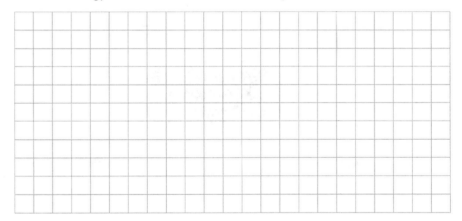

8. How much electrical energy will a 40.0 W light bulb use if it is left on for 10.0 h? Use the unit kWh for your response. Show your work below. **A**

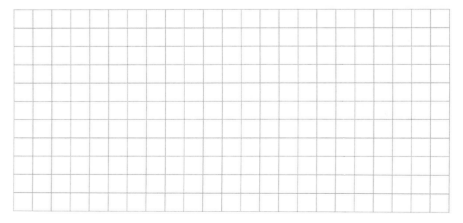

Explore Applications of Renewable Energy Sources

Going Off the Grid

Vocabulary

brownout   electrical power grid

MAIN IDEA: Individuals and families can reduce their reliance on the power grid by generating their own electricity. Wind turbines and photovoltaic systems are two methods of off-the-grid electrical energy generation.

1. Organize what you know about residential photovoltaic systems OR residential wind turbine systems by filling in the main ideas web below. C A

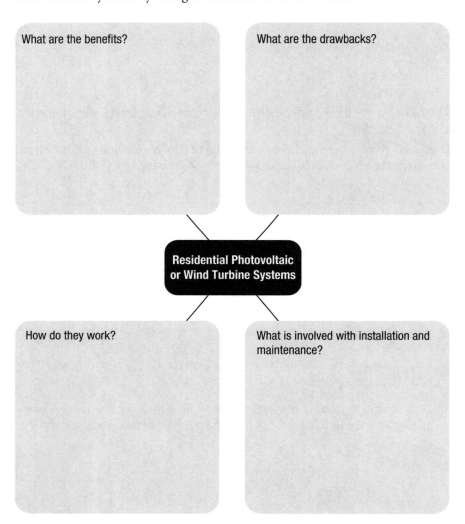

What are the benefits?

What are the drawbacks?

Residential Photovoltaic or Wind Turbine Systems

How do they work?

What is involved with installation and maintenance?

2. What sources of research provided the most useful information about these topics? C A

Work, Energy, Power, and Society

Fill in the graphic organizer below to summarize the main ideas from Chapter 5.

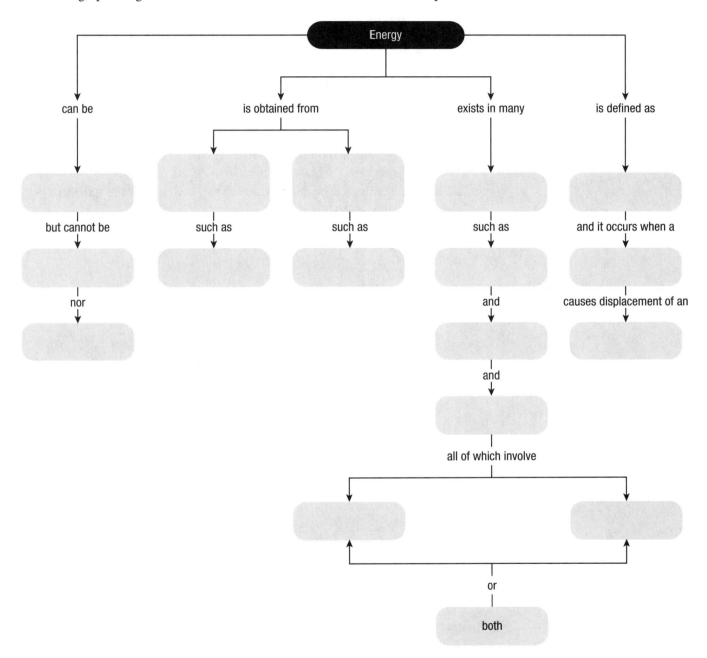

K/U   Knowledge/Understanding
T/I   Thinking/Investigation
C   Communication
A   Application

1. What is the SI unit for work? (5.1) K/U
   (a) newton metre, or joule
   (b) metres per second
   (c) kilowatt hours
   (d) joules per second, or watts

2. A baseball that is moving through the air after being thrown has
   (a) gravitational potential energy only
   (b) kinetic energy only
   (c) both gravitational potential energy and kinetic energy
   (d) neither gravitational potential energy nor kinetic energy (5.2) K/U

3. Indicate whether each statement is true or false. If you think the statement is false, rewrite it to make it true.
   (a) The form of energy associated with randomly moving atoms and molecules is electrical energy. (5.3) K/U

   (b) Hydroelectricity is a renewable energy resource. (5.4) K/U

4. What equation would you use to determine the amount of work done when you push a box of books with a force of 40.0 N and the box moves 2.5 m in the direction in which the force acts? Provide the equation, then solve. (5.1) K/U

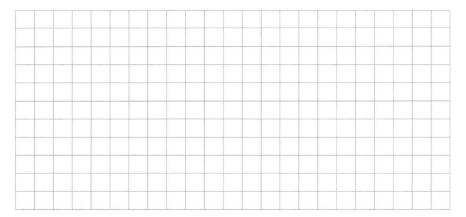

5. Describe the energy transformations that occur when you turn on an electric radio. Then, explain how the law of conservation of energy applies to these energy transformations. (5.3) T/I A

6. You run two trials of a 50 m dash. Your time in the first trial is 1 s faster than your time in the second trial. Compare the work done and power produced in the two trials. (5.5) **A**

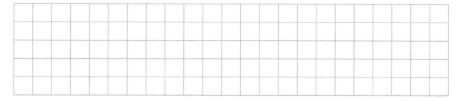

7. Fill in the graphic organizer with the following terms to order the efficiency with which the devices or processes transform energy. (5.4) **T/I**
   - gasoline-powered vehicle
   - photosynthesis
   - bicycle
   - electric vehicle
   - hydroelectric power plant

   Increasing efficiency ⟶

   (a)   (b)   (c)   (d)   (e)

8. Sequence the steps of electrical energy generation that occur in a hydroelectric power plant. (5.4) **T/I** **C** **A**
   - Electrical energy is distributed through power lines to homes.
   - Water from the reservoir moves through the penstock.
   - The turbine, which is connected to a generator, spins.
   - Water gains kinetic energy and strikes the blades of the turbine.

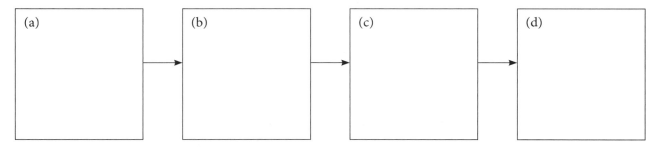

9. In the space below, make a Venn diagram that compares solar panels and wind turbines. (5.6) **T/I** **C** **A**

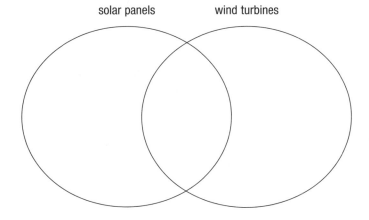

solar panels   wind turbines

Warmth and Coldness

Textbook pp. 270–274

> **Vocabulary**
>
> kinetic molecular theory   Fahrenheit scale   freezing point
>
> thermal energy   Kelvin scale   boiling point
>
> temperature   melting point   condensation point
>
> Celsius scale

MAIN IDEA: Thermal energy is the total potential energy and the total kinetic energy possessed by the particles of a substance.

1. The SI unit used to measure thermal energy is the _____. K/U

2. The thermal energy of a substance includes both the _____ and the _____ of the particles of the substance. K/U

3. The _____ of the particles of a substance is associated with the motion of the particles. K/U

4. The _____ of the particles of a substance is associated with the force of attraction between the particles. K/U

MAIN IDEA: Temperature is a measure of the average kinetic energy of the particles in a substance.

5. Compare and contrast the thermal energy of a substance and the temperature of the substance. Identify one way they are similar and one way they are different. T/I C

MAIN IDEA: The kinetic molecular theory states that as particles of matter gain kinetic energy, they move faster and the temperature of the substance increases. Similarly, as particles of matter lose kinetic energy, they move more slowly and the temperature of the substance decreases.

6. Fill in the flow chart using the words *increases* and *decreases* to describe the relationship between the temperature of a substance and the kinetic energy of the particles of the substance. K/U C

> **STUDY TIP**
>
> **Flow Charts**
> You can use flow charts to summarize the steps in a process. In this case, you can use the flow chart to visualize the changes that occur as particles gain or lose energy. Try reading the steps aloud to a partner after you have completed the flow chart.

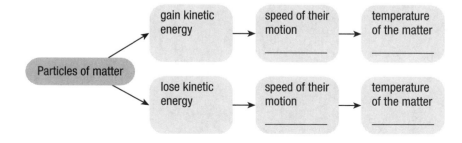

MAIN IDEA: Temperature can be measured using the Celsius scale, Fahrenheit scale, or Kelvin scale. Scientists typically use the Kelvin scale because kelvins are SI units.

7. Fill in the blanks below to describe the Fahrenheit and Celsius scales. K/U

   Celsius scale

       Created by: _____

       Boiling point of pure water: _____

       Freezing point of pure water: _____

   Fahrenheit scale

       Created by: _____

       Boiling point of pure water: _____

       Freezing point of pure water: _____

8. Describe the motion of particles in a substance at absolute 0, or 0 K. T/I

MAIN IDEA: The equations $T_C = T_K - 273$ and $T_K = T_C + 273$ can be used to convert temperatures from one scale to the other.

9. Fill in **Table 1** below to practise converting temperatures from one scale to another. T/I

Table 1 Temperature Conversions

Celsius	Kelvin
45 °C	
	120 K
−12 °C	

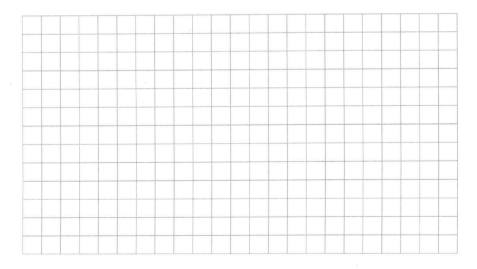

Heat

Textbook pp. 275–280

Vocabulary

heat

thermal conduction

convection

convection current

radiation

thermal conductor

thermal insulator

MAIN IDEA: Thermal energy is the total amount of kinetic energy and potential energy of the particles in a substance.

1. What two types of energy make up the thermal energy of a substance? K/U

2. The thermal energy in the particles of a substance determines the _____ of the substance. K/U

3. Two objects of the same mass and the same material that have the same thermal energy will have the same _____. K/U

4. Fill in the missing terms in the concept map below to describe the relationship between changes in thermal energy and changes in temperature. T/I

STUDY TIP

Concept Maps
You can use concept maps to learn how ideas are related. After you have completed this concept map, explain what happens when the particles of a substance absorb energy.

5. As described in the concept map above, the energy that a substance absorbs changes both the potential energy and the kinetic energy of the particles of the substance. Is the percentage of the added energy that changes kinetic energy and the percentage of the added energy that changes potential energy the same for all substances, or does it vary between substances? K/U

MAIN IDEA: Heat is the transfer of thermal energy from a warmer object to a cooler one.

6. Contrast the meaning of the terms *heat* and *thermal energy*. K/U C

MAIN IDEA: Thermal energy can be transferred in three different ways: by thermal conduction, by convection, or by radiation.

7. Fill in **Table 1** below to describe conduction, convection, and radiation. K/U

Table 1 Thermal Energy Transfer

Type of thermal energy transfer	Definition	Everyday example
conduction		
convection		
radiation		

8. Define the following terms in your own words: K/U
   (a) thermal conductor

   (b) thermal insulator

9. Give an example of a material that is a good thermal conductor. K/U

10. Give an example of a material that is a good thermal insulator. K/U

Heat Capacity

Textbook pp. 281–287

Vocabulary

specific heat capacity (c)   principle of thermal energy exchange   thermal contraction

quantity of heat (Q)   thermal expansion

MAIN IDEA: Specific heat capacity is the amount of heat needed to raise the temperature of a 1 kg sample of a substance by 1 °C.

Table 1 Specific Heat Capacities

Substance	Specific heat capacity (J/(kg•°C))
water	4.18×10^3
ethyl alcohol	2.46×10^3
ice	2.1×10^3
aluminum	9.2×10^2
glass	8.4×10^2
iron	4.5×10^2
copper	3.8×10^2
silver	2.4×10^2
lead	1.3×10^2

1. If 10 J of energy are added to 0.1 kg of each substance shown in **Table 1** above, which substance will experience the greatest change in temperature? T/I

2. If 10 J of energy are added to 0.1 kg of each substance shown in Table 1 above, which substance will experience the least change in temperature? T/I

3. Explain the reasoning you used to arrive at your answers for Questions 1 and 2. T/I C A

LEARNING TIP

Mass Must Be in Kilograms When Using the Quantity of Heat Equation
Since the units for specific heat capacity are joules per kilogram degree Celsius, mass must be expressed in kilograms when using the quantity of heat equation.

MAIN IDEA: The quantity of heat, or amount of thermal energy absorbed or released by an object, can be calculated using the equation $Q = mc\Delta T$.

4. In the spaces below, identify the meaning of and the units used for each variable in the equation $Q = mc\Delta T$. K/U

   (a) Q stands for _____ measured in units of _____.

   (b) m stands for _____ measured in units of _____.

(c) *c* stands for _____ measured in units of _____.

(d) ΔT stands for _____ measured in units of _____.

5. When a 23 kg block of iron is heated from 25 °C to 65 °C, how much thermal energy is absorbed by the iron? Use the space below for your calculations. T/I

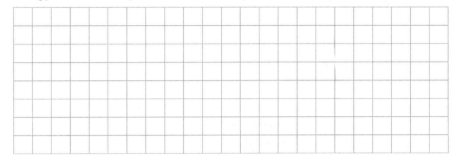

STUDY **TIP**

Calculations
When reviewing equations used for calculations, be sure to note the units for the variables in the equation.

MAIN IDEA: The principle of heat exchange states that thermal energy moves from a warm object to a cooler one until both objects reach a new constant temperature. This principle can be represented by the equation $Q_{released} + Q_{absorbed} = 0$.

6. Does the equation $Q_{released} + Q_{absorbed} = 0$ reflect the law of conservation of energy? Explain why or why not. T/I C

7. What assumption is made when using the equation $Q_{released} + Q_{absorbed} = 0$ to describe thermal energy exchange? Is this assumption realistic in everyday settings? T/I C

MAIN IDEA: The absorption or release of thermal energy results in thermal expansion or contraction.

8. An increase in the thermal energy of a substance causes the particles to spread out, resulting in _____. K/U

9. A decrease in the thermal energy of a substance causes the particles to move closer together, resulting in _____. K/U

10. Identify an everyday object that has been designed to accommodate thermal expansion and contraction, and describe specifically how the object's design allows for thermal expansion and contraction. T/I

States of Matter and Changes of State

Textbook pp. 288–295

Vocabulary

fusion	latent heat (Q)	specific latent heat (L)
heating graph	latent heat of fusion	specific latent heat of fusion (L_f)
cooling graph	latent heat of vaporization	specific latent heat of vaporization (L_v)

MAIN IDEA: The three states of matter are solid, liquid, and gas. When thermal energy is released or absorbed, a change in state may happen.

1. Label the states of matter in **Figure 1** below. K/U

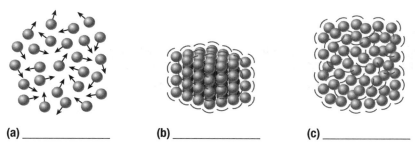

(a) _____ (b) _____ (c) _____

Figure 1

2. Complete the statements to describe what happens in **Figure 2** below. Use the terms *increases*, *decreases*, or *remains unchanged* to fill in the blanks. T/I

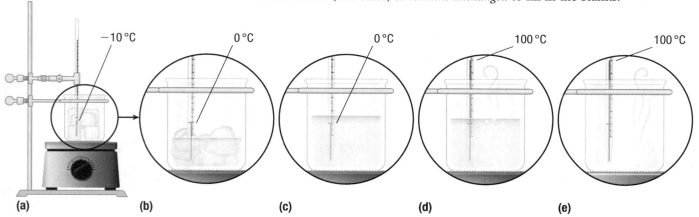

(a)   (b)   (c)   (d)   (e)

Figure 2

Between (a) and (b), thermal energy _____ and temperature _____.

Between (b) and (c), thermal energy _____ and temperature _____.

Between (c) and (d), thermal energy _____ and temperature _____.

Between (d) and (e), thermal energy _____ and temperature _____.

3. In some of the descriptions in Question 2, thermal energy increased, yet temperature remained unchanged. How can this occur if energy is conserved? T/I A

MAIN IDEA: The change in temperature that occurs as a substance releases or absorbs thermal energy can be shown in a cooling graph or a heating graph.

4. The vertical dotted lines in **Figure 3** divide the graph into five sections, from left to right. Make an X on any section that represents a change of state. T/I

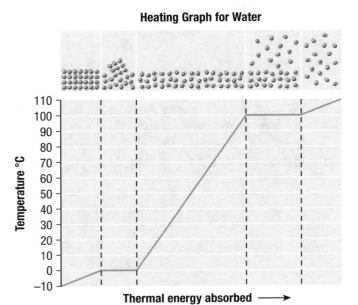

Figure 3

5. If the vertical axis of the graph in Figure 3 was labelled "Thermal Energy" rather than "Temperature," would the line have the same shape? Explain. T/I

MAIN IDEA: The thermal energy that is absorbed or released during a change of state is called the latent heat of the substance. If the substance is melting or freezing, it is called latent heat of fusion. If the substance is evaporating or condensing, it is called the latent heat of vaporization.

6. What is the SI unit for latent heat? K/U
   (a) joules
   (b) degrees
   (c) calories
   (d) watts

7. Latent heat of fusion is the amount of energy absorbed when a substance _____ or released when a substance _____. K/U

8. Latent heat of vaporization is the amount of energy absorbed when a substance _____ or released when the substance _____. K/U

MAIN IDEA: The specific latent heat of fusion (L_f) is the amount of thermal energy per kilogram needed to melt or freeze a substance. The specific latent heat of vaporization (L_v) is the amount of thermal energy needed per kilogram to evaporate or condense a substance.

9. For any specific substance, explain why a single value can be used for both the latent heat associated with melting and the latent heat associated with freezing. K/U

MAIN IDEA: The equation $Q = mL_f$ is used to calculate the latent heat of fusion, and $Q = mL_v$ is used to calculate the latent heat of vaporization.

10. How much thermal energy is absorbed by a 22 g ice cube as it melts? The specific latent heat of fusion of water is 3.4×10^5 J/kg. Use the space below for your calculations. T/I

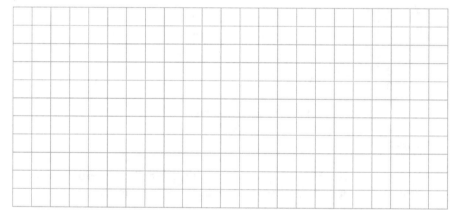

MAIN IDEA: Ice is one of the few solids that floats in its liquid; this is due to the shape of its molecules and the forces of attraction between its molecules.

11. As the temperature of a sample of water changes from 20 °C to 0 °C, how does its volume change? K/U

12. Describe one practical consideration related to your answer to Question 11. T/I

Heating and Cooling Systems

Textbook pp. 296–299

Vocabulary

electrical heating system

forced-air heating system

hot water heating system

geothermal system

MAIN IDEA: All heating systems have a source of thermal energy, a means of transferring the energy, and a thermostat to control the production and distribution of energy. Conventional heating systems use either electricity or fossil fuels as a source of thermal energy.

1. Compare and contrast forced-air heating systems and hot water heating systems. Identify one way they are similar and one way they are different. K/U

MAIN IDEA: Conventional cooling systems use the evaporation of pressurized refrigerants to absorb thermal energy from the air, resulting in cool air that can then be blown through a duct system.

2. Fill in the cycle diagram below to describe how cooling systems work. Use the following sentences to fill in the cycle diagram: K/U
   - Warm refrigerant gas releases thermal energy and changes to a liquid.
   - Liquid refrigerant evaporates into a gas.
   - Liquid refrigerant absorbs thermal energy from surroundings.
   - Temperature of refrigerant gas increases.

> ### STUDY **TIP**
>
> **Cycle Diagrams**
> You can use a cycle diagram to learn about a process that occurs in a series of repeating steps. When you have completed this cycle diagram, use it to review how a cooling system works.

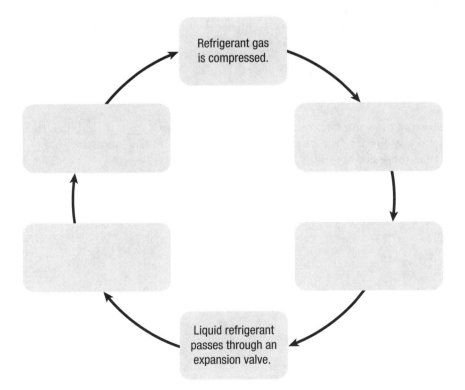

Refrigerant gas is compressed.

Liquid refrigerant passes through an expansion valve.

MAIN IDEA: A typical thermostat uses a bimetallic strip and a mercury switch to turn a heating or cooling system on or off as temperatures change.

3. Use the concepts of thermal expansion and contraction to explain why a bimetallic strip, rather than a strip made of a single type of metal, is used in many thermostats. T/I A

MAIN IDEA: Conventional heating and cooling systems produce greenhouse gases such as carbon dioxide, so they are not considered environmentally friendly.

4. Identify one specific way in which conventional heating systems can damage the environment, and one specific way in which conventional cooling systems can damage the environment. K/U C

MAIN IDEA: Geothermal systems use Earth's natural thermal energy for heating and cooling purposes. In the winter, thermal energy is transferred from below Earth's surface into a building to heat it. In the summer, thermal energy is transferred from a building into Earth's surface to cool it.

5. Indicate whether the following statement is true or false. If you think it is false, rewrite it to make it true: In a geothermal system, thermal energy in Earth's crust is used to heat and cool homes. K/U

6. During the winter, temperatures underground are _____ than those above ground. In the summer, the temperatures underground are _____ than those above ground. K/U

Geothermal Systems: Friend or Foe?

Textbook pp. 300–301

MAIN IDEA: Geothermal systems are an alternative to conventional heating and cooling systems. There are benefits and drawbacks associated with geothermal systems.

1. Use **Table 1** below to analyze the benefits and risks and costs of geothermal systems. T/I C

Table 1 Benefits and Costs of Geothermal Systems

Benefits	Risks and Costs

STUDY TIP

Using Tables
You can use a table to organize information you find during research. In this case, the table allows you to organize and visualize the costs and benefits of geothermal systems. Use this table to weigh the costs and benefits and to develop an opinion about geothermal systems.

2. Based on what you have recorded in the table, do you think the benefits of geothermal systems outweigh the risks and costs? Explain. T/I C

Physics JOURNAL

When a Brewer Becomes a Scientist

MAIN IDEA: Although James Prescott Joule did not start his career as a scientist, his work led to a dramatic change in our understanding of thermal energy.

1. How did Joule's love of science first develop? K/U

2. Were Joule's early results well received by the scientific community? Why or why not? K/U

3. Describe the understanding of thermal energy that most scientists of Joule's time shared. K/U

STUDY TIP

Asking Questions
Questions about a reading passage can be used to help you understand the main ideas. After you complete a reading, ask yourself or a partner questions about the main ideas of the reading. Use your answers to reinforce what you have read.

4. How did Joule's understanding of thermal energy differ from the prevailing scientific idea of his time? K/U

5. Explain how Joule demonstrated that mechanical energy could be transformed into thermal energy. K/U

6. Was Joule's work eventually accepted? Explain. K/U

Thermal Energy and Society

Fill in the graphic organizer below to summarize the concepts you learned in Chapter 6. You can use graphic organizers like this one to create your own study notes for the chapter.

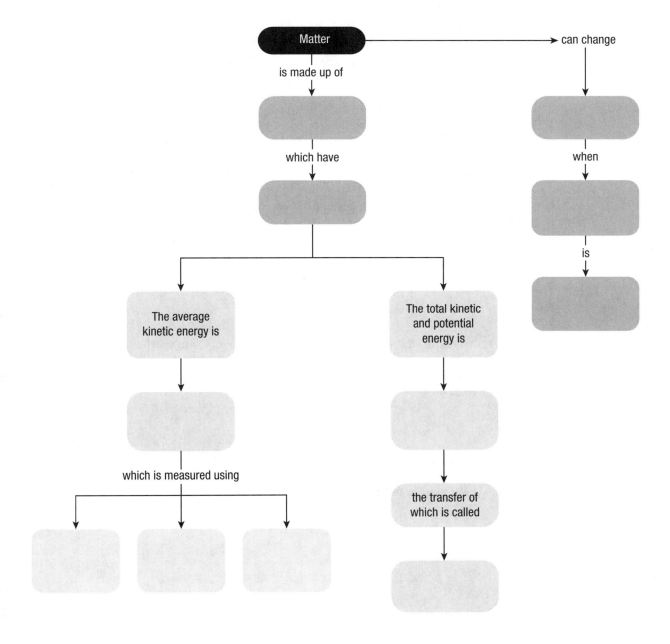

K/U Knowledge/Understanding
T/I Thinking/Investigation
C   Communication
A   Application

1. At which temperature do the particles of a substance have the least kinetic energy? (6.1) K/U
   (a) 212 °F
   (b) 100 °C
   (c) 100 K
   (d) −273 °C

2. Which of the following is classified as a thermal conductor? (6.2) K/U
   (a) wool
   (b) copper
   (c) air
   (d) plastic

3. Indicate whether each statement is true or false. If you think the statement is false, rewrite it to make it true. K/U
   (a) The specific heat capacity of water is high in comparison to most common liquids. (6.3)

   (b) The particles of an ice cube have greater kinetic energy than the particles in a cup of liquid water. (6.4)

4. You taste a bit of soup, and it burns your tongue. You set the soup aside for several minutes, and then taste the soup again. Now it can be eaten. Explain what has occurred in terms of the kinetic energy of the particles of the soup. (6.1) T/I A

5. When a 42 kg block of copper is heated from 25 °C to 37 °C, how much thermal energy is absorbed by the copper? Use the space below for your calculations. (6.3) T/I

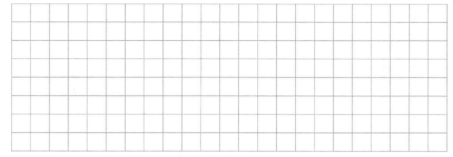

6. Identify one benefit of geothermal systems and one risk or cost of geothermal systems. (6.6) T/I

7. Three qualities that many scientists possess are curiosity, perseverance, and independent thinking. Choose one of these qualities, and describe how that quality was displayed by James Prescott Joule. (6.7) C A

8. Complete **Table 1** below with the following terms: *freezing point, boiling point, melting point, condensation point.* (6.1) K/U C

Table 1 Temperature and Physical State

	temperature at which liquid changes to gas
	temperature at which solid changes to liquid
	temperature at which gas changes to liquid
	temperature at which liquid changes to solid

9. Complete the concept map below with the terms *convection, radiation,* and *conduction.* (6.2) K/U C

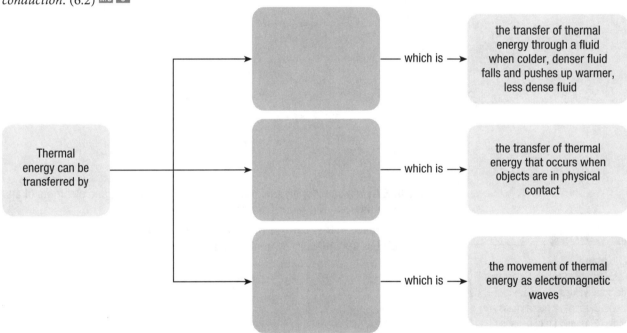

10. Fill in the flow chart below to describe what happens as a sample of water is cooled from 110 °C to −10 °C. Use the following phrases: (6.4) T/I C
   - water vapour condenses into liquid water
   - water vapour cools down
   - ice cools down
   - liquid water freezes into ice
   - liquid water cools down

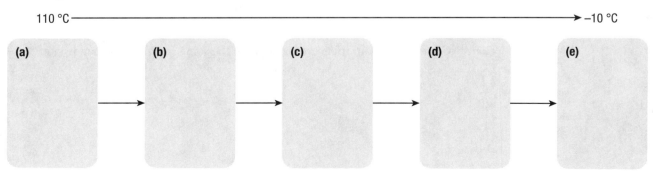

Atoms and Isotopes

Textbook pp. 318–322

Vocabulary		
proton	ground state	isotope
neutron	excited state	radioisotope
nucleons	atomic number	radiation
electron	mass number	

MAIN IDEA: The Bohr–Rutherford model of the atom illustrates the atomic structure of an element.

1. List the four main discoveries that were combined to create the Bohr–Rutherford model of the atom. K/U

   (i)

   (ii)

   (iii)

   (iv)

MAIN IDEA: You can identify the number of protons, neutrons, and electrons of an element from its Bohr–Rutherford model.

2. In the space below, draw a Bohr–Rutherford model of a potassium atom, which has 19 protons, 20 neutrons, and 19 electrons. T/I C

> **LEARNING TIP**
>
> **Mass Numbers**
> The mass numbers of most elements have decimal values associated with them. Carbon-12 has a mass of exactly 12 atomic units because it is the substance to which all other elements are compared by atomic mass. The mass number that appears in the periodic table for carbon is slightly higher than 12 because of the small amounts of carbon-14 that exist in nature.

3. Contrast an atom in its ground state to the same atom in an excited state. T/I

MAIN IDEA: You can identify the mass number and atomic number of an element from the periodic table.

4. Label the atomic number and mass number of neon on **Figure 1** below. K/U

| 10 |
| **Ne** |
| neon |
| 20.18 |

Figure 1

5. The atomic number of an atom is equal to the number of _____ in the atom. K/U

6. The mass number of an atom is equal to the number of _____ in the atom. K/U

MAIN IDEA: Isotopes of an element have the same number of protons but different numbers of neutrons.

7. Fill in **Table 1** below to compare and contrast carbon-12 and carbon-14, two isotopes of carbon. T/I

Table 1 Comparing Isotopes of Carbon

	Carbon-12	**Carbon-14**
atomic symbol		
atomic number		
mass number		
number of protons		
number of neutrons		
number of electrons		

MAIN IDEA: Radioactive isotopes are unstable and will spontaneously undergo a change in their atomic structure.

8. Define the following terms: K/U

   (a) radioisotope:

   (b) radiation:

MAIN IDEA: Some radioactive isotopes have useful applications, such as medical diagnosis and therapy.

9. Describe radionuclide therapy and explain how it is used to treat cancer. T/I C

Radioactive Decay

Vocabulary

radioactivity	alpha (α) decay	beta (β) decay
nuclear fission	alpha particle	beta particle
nuclear reaction	parent atom	positron
electrostatic force	daughter atom	photon
strong nuclear force	transmutation	gamma (λ) decay
radioactive decay		

STUDY TIP

Concept Maps
You can use a concept map to show how ideas are related. In this case, the concept map can be used to review information about the forces that act on nuclear particles.

MAIN IDEA: The strong nuclear force is responsible for holding the nucleus of an atom together by balancing the proton-proton electrostatic forces of repulsion.

1. Fill in the concept map below with the following terms: nucleons, protons, electrostatic force, strong nuclear force. [K/U]

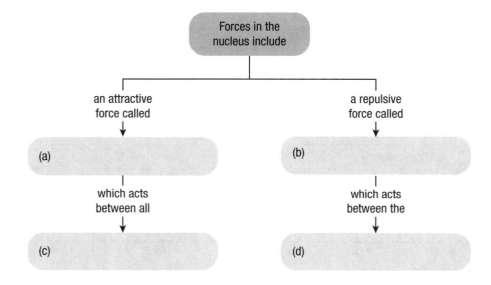

MAIN IDEA: Nuclear reactions are reactions that involve the nucleus of an atom, where high-energy electromagnetic radiation is either emitted or absorbed.

2. Compare and contrast chemical reactions and nuclear reactions. Identify one way that they are similar and one way that they are different. [T/I]

MAIN IDEA: Radioactive decay is a process by which the nucleus of a radioisotope spontaneously changes.

3. Describe the relative sizes of the electrostatic forces and the strong nuclear forces in an unstable atom. [K/U]

MAIN IDEA: There are three common types of radioactive decay: alpha decay, beta decay, and gamma decay.

4. Fill in **Table 1** below to describe common types of radioactive decay. K/U

Table 1 Radioactive Decay

Type of decay	Change in atomic mass	Change in atomic number
alpha decay		
beta-negative decay		
beta-positive decay		
electron capture		
gamma decay		

5. Write the equation that shows uranium-238 undergoing alpha decay to form thorium (Th). T/I A

6. Write the general equation for beta-positive decay. K/U

7. How is the general equation for beta-negative decay different from the equation for beta-positive decay? K/U

8. In the equation for gamma decay, what change occurs between the parent and daughter nuclei? K/U

MAIN IDEA: Alpha particles, beta particles, and gamma rays are forms of ionizing radiation.

9. Define the term "ionizing radiation". K/U

10. Why must living tissue be protected from ionizing radiation? K/U

7.2 Radioactive Decay **111**

Half-Life

> **Vocabulary**
>
> half-life

MAIN IDEA: The half-life of a radioactive isotope is the amount of time required for it to decay to one-half of its original mass. Half-life can be calculated using the equation $A = A_0\left(\dfrac{1}{2}\right)^{\frac{t}{h}}$. The decay of a radioactive isotope can be mathematically modelled using a table, a graph, or an equation.

STUDY TIP

Using Tables
Tables can be used to organize information. In this case, the table shows how the mass of the sample changes over time. Work with a partner to find one other way to organize or display this data.

1. Fill in **Table 1** below to show how radioactive decay occurs. K/U

Table 1 Radioactive Decay of Gold-198

Number of half lives	Mass of sample remaining
original sample	120 g
after 1 half-life (2.6 days)	
after 2 half-lives (5.2 days)	
after 3 half-lives (7.8 days)	
after 4 half-lives (10.4 days)	

LEARNING TIP

The Half-Life Equation
The exponent t/h is time divided by half-life. This quotient represents the number of half-lives, which is the number of times the initial amount is reduced by one half.

2. Carbon-15 has a half-life of 2.5 s. Use the half-life equation to determine the mass of carbon-15 that will remain from a 5.0×10^2 mg initial sample after 14 s. Use the space below for your calculations. T/I

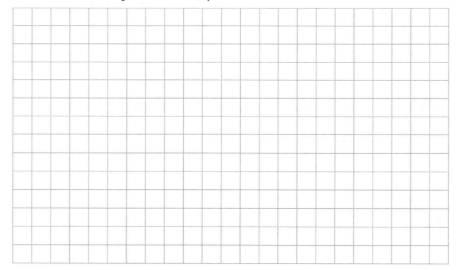

MAIN IDEA: Half-lives can vary from a tiny fraction of a second to millions of years.

3. The length of half-lives varies greatly, but for each isotope, _____ % of the existing sample decays during the period of a half-life. K/U

MAIN IDEA: Some isotopes, like carbon-14 and aluminum-26, have useful applications due in part to their particular half-lives. Carbon-14 is a useful isotope for dating fossils and other archaeological objects.

4. Explain how carbon-14 becomes incorporated in the bodies of living things. ▪T/I▪

5. What is an application of aluminum-26 dating? ▪K/U▪

Use the decay curve for C-14 shown in **Figure 1** to answer questions 6 and 7.

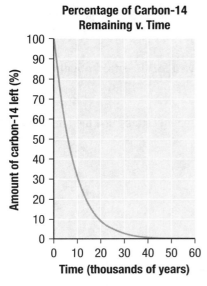

Percentage of Carbon-14 Remaining v. Time

Amount of carbon-14 left (%)

Time (thousands of years)

Figure 1

6. The remains of two different organisms are analyzed. The first organism has 9 % of its original C-14 remaining. The second organism has 30 % of its original C-14 remaining. ▪T/I▪
   (a) What is the approximate age of the remains of the first organism?

   (b) What is the approximate age of the remains of the second organism?

7. Why is carbon-14 rather than carbon-15 used for radioactive dating of the remains of organisms? ▪A▪

Nuclear Fission and Nuclear Power Generation

Textbook pp. 334–341

Vocabulary

atomic mass unit (u)	binding energy	chain reaction
mass defect	mega-electron volt (MeV)	

MAIN IDEA: Albert Einstein was the first person to propose that mass and energy are equivalent and related by $E = mc^2$.

1. Restate the equation $E = mc^2$ in words. **T/I**

2. In the equation $E = mc^2$, what value is used for the speed of light? **K/U**

MAIN IDEA: The law of conservation of mass–energy states that the total mass–energy in any reaction remains constant.

3. Define the following terms: **K/U**
   (a) atomic mass unit

   (b) binding energy

4. An atomic mass unit, which is a unit of mass, is much _____ than a kilogram. A mega-electron volt, which is used to measure energy, is much _____ than a joule. **T/I**

MAIN IDEA: Very large amounts of energy are released during a nuclear fission reaction; the amount of released energy is equivalent to the mass defect.

5. Define the term *chain reaction*. **K/U**

6. When the mass of the electrons and nucleons in an atom is added together, the sum is always _____ than the actual atomic mass. The difference is known as the _____ _____, which can be multiplied by _____ to find the binding energy of the nucleus. **K/U**

7. What information do you need to calculate the mass defect of an atom? **K/U**

MAIN IDEA: CANDU fission reactors use only natural uranium as a fuel and heavy water as a moderator.

8. A diagram of a CANDU nuclear reactor is shown in **Figure 1** below. Fill in the missing labels. K/U

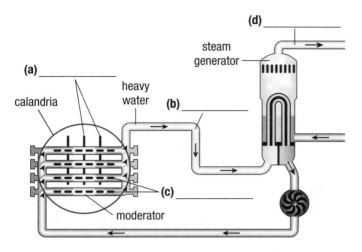

Figure 1 CANDU nuclear reactor

9. What is the calandria? K/U

10. What is the function of the moderator? K/U

11. (a) What are the differences between heavy water and regular water?

    (b) How is heavy water used in a nuclear reactor? K/U

MAIN IDEA: Nuclear waste disposal is a complex issue whose long-term solution is still under development.

12. Identify two factors that must be considered in the disposal of nuclear waste. K/U

Nuclear Fusion

> **Vocabulary**
>
> nuclear fusion

MAIN IDEA: Nuclear fusion is the process by which lighter atoms fuse together to form heavier atoms.

1. Is the following statement accurate? Explain your response. "Nuclear fusion is the opposite of nuclear fission." [T/I]

2. How does the binding energy change when a heavy nucleus splits? [T/I]

3. How does the binding energy change when two light nuclei fuse? [T/I]

4. For both nuclear fusion and nuclear fission, the products are more _____ than the reactants. [K/U]

MAIN IDEA: Nuclear fusion reactions are exothermic and produce significantly more energy per mass of fuel than fission reactions.

5. Look at **Figure 1** showing the relationship between binding energy and mass number. Summarize how the slope of the line for mass numbers 80 and higher compares to the slope of the line for mass numbers 20 and lower. Summarize how this relates to the relative amount of energy produced by fission reactions and fusion reactions. [T/I] [A]

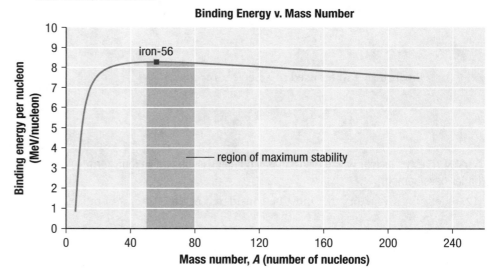

Figure 1 Binding energy v. mass number

6. (a) What are the advantages of nuclear fusion as an energy source? K/U

   (b) Why is nuclear fusion not used exclusively as an energy source? K/U

7. Determine the energy released when a neutron and a proton fuse to form deuterium. The mass defect is 0.002388 u.

MAIN IDEA: Magnetic confinement fusion is a method in which electromagnetic forces are used to confine fusion fuel that is in a very high-temperature, plasma state.

LEARNING TIP

Superconducting Electromagnets
A superconductor is a material with little to no electrical resistance. A superconducting electromagnet produces powerful magnetic fields when current is applied. You will learn more about electromagnets in Chapter 13.

8. Add the following labels to **Figure 2**: transfer coil, toroidal field coil, plasma, plasma current. K/U

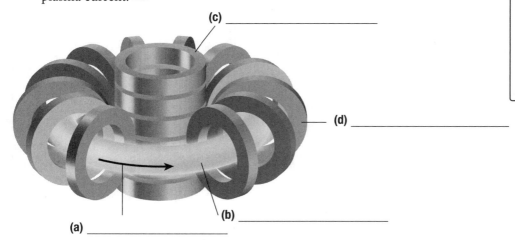

(c) _____

(d) _____

(b) _____

(a) _____

Figure 2 Magnetic confinement fusion

9. Describe the function of the magnetic confinement fusion reactor shown in Figure 2. T/I

10. In order to make a fusion reaction sustainable, what must occur in the fusion reactor? K/U

11. Name two processes by which stellar fusion occurs. K/U

MAIN IDEA: The ITER project is the first significant international attempt to create a functioning nuclear fusion research reactor.

12. Fill in **Table 1** below to describe the pros and cons of the ITER project. K/U

Table 1 ITER Project

Potential benefits	Costs and risks

Pest Control

Textbook pp. 348–349

MAIN IDEA: Nuclear pest control is a new field of scientific study with benefits as well as costs and risks. Nuclear pest control involves sterilizing organisms so that they cannot reproduce.

1. Summarize information about using nuclear technology for pest control by filling in the fishbone diagram below. K/U C

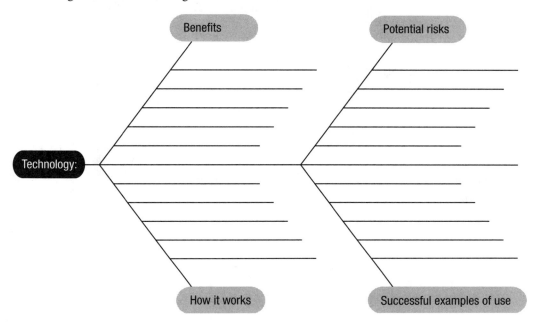

2. Based on the information you recorded above, do you think the advantages of nuclear pest control outweigh the risks, or do you think the risks outweigh the benefits? Explain your response. T/I C

Nuclear Energy and Society

Complete this graphic organizer to summarize what you learned in Chapter 7, adding additional notes, equations, and diagrams that will help you to review the concepts in this chapter.

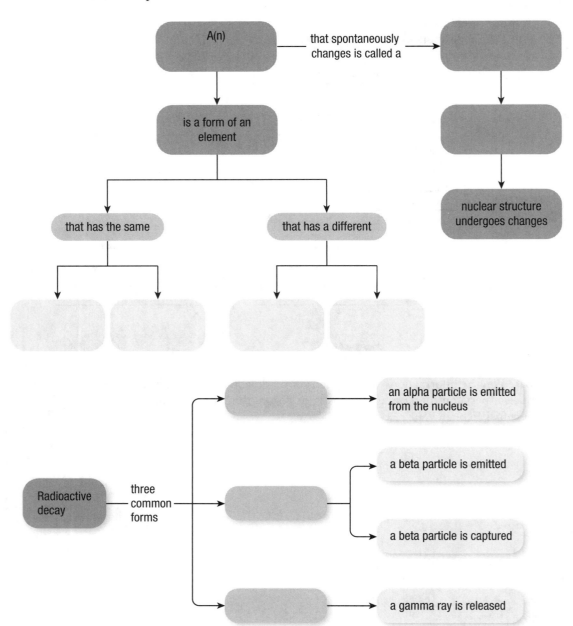

1. Carbon-12 and carbon-14 are different isotopes of carbon, so they have different
   (a) mass numbers
   (b) chemical symbols
   (c) atomic numbers
   (d) numbers of protons (7.1) K/U

2. An alpha particle consists of
   (a) three protons
   (b) two protons and two neutrons
   (c) energy, but no particles
   (d) one electron (7.2) K/U

3. Indicate whether each statement is true or false. If you think it is false, rewrite it to make it true. K/U
   (a) After two half-lives, 25 % of the original sample of a radioactive material remains. (7.3)

   (b) CANDU reactors use only plutonium as a nuclear fuel. (7.4)

4. Use an equation to show how mass number and atomic number change during alpha decay. (7.2) K/U

5. (a) Summarize the meaning of the equation $E = mc^2$.

   (b) Determine the energy change that would occur as the result of a mass defect of 0.003695 u. (7.4) K/U T/I

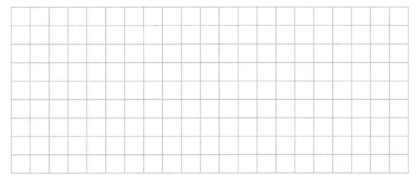

6. Describe the process of nuclear fusion and identify the size of nuclei likely to be found in stars. (7.5) K/U T/I

7. Identify one benefit and one risk associated with the use of nuclear technology for pest control. Then, give your opinion about this technology. (7.6) K/U T/I

8. Complete the following comparison matrix to compare protons, neutrons, and electrons. (7.1, 7.4) K/U

	Proton	Neutron	Electron
charge			
location			

9. Add the following terms to the table below to classify types of decay as transmutation or not transmutation: alpha decay, beta-negative decay, beta-positive decay, electron capture, gamma decay. (7.2) K/U

Transmutation	Not transmutation

10. Sequence the energy transformations that occur in a CANDU reactor facility. Use the following terms in the flow chart below: thermal energy, electrical energy, mechanical energy, nuclear energy. (7.4) K/U

(a)   →   (b)   →   (c)   →   (d)

11. Fill in the concept map below to summarize information about fission and fusion reactions. (7.4, 7.5) K/U

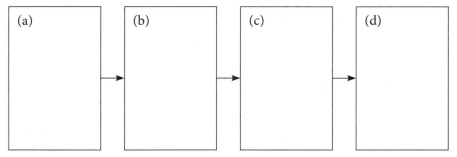

During nuclear fission and nuclear fusion

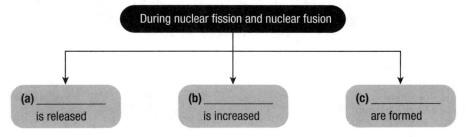

(a) _____ is released

(b) _____ is increased

(c) _____ are formed

1. The law of conservation of energy states that energy can be
   (a) destroyed
   (b) transformed
   (c) created
   (d) lost (5.3) K/U

2. Which of the following is a non-renewable source of energy? (5.4) K/U
   (a) hydroelectricity
   (b) geothermal
   (c) biofuels
   (d) natural gas

3. Indicate whether each statement is true or false. If you think the statement is false, rewrite it to make it true. K/U
   (a) Absolute zero is equivalent to 0° on the Fahrenheit scale. (6.1)

   (b) For any substance, the latent heat of fusion is the amount of thermal energy required to change a solid into a liquid or a liquid into a solid. (6.4)

4. How much power is produced by a runner who transforms 32 kJ of energy into kinetic and thermal energy in 16 s during a sprint? (5.5) T/I A

5. A refrigerator is a cooling system that transfers thermal energy from one location to another. Identify the location that thermal energy is moved from, and the location that thermal energy is moved to when a refrigerator is functioning. (6.5) K/U A

6. A friend explains that after one half-life, 50 % of the original sample of a radioactive substance is decayed; therefore, after two half-lives, 100 % of the sample must be decayed. Is your friend correct? Why or why not? (7.3) T/I A

7. Explain how nuclear fission and fusion affect nuclear stability. (7.5) K/U

8. Fill in **Table 1** to describe the kinetic energy, the gravitational potential energy, and the mechanical energy of the listed objects. Use the terms *increasing*, *decreasing*, or *constant* to fill in the table. (5.2) K/U

Table 1 Energy of Moving Objects

Object	Kinetic energy	Gravitational potential energy	Mechanical energy
airplane moving at a constant velocity and altitude			
snowflake falling from a cloud			
car moving at steady speed along a level road			

9. Fill in the graphic organizer about below changes in state. The arrows represent increases and decreases in thermal energy. Use the following terms to complete the graphic organizer: gas, condensing, freezing, solid, boiling, gas, melting. (6.4) K/U C

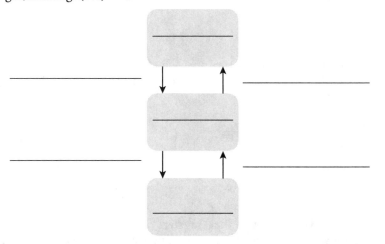

10. Fill in the Venn diagram to compare and contrast beta-negative decay and beta-positive decay. (7.2) T/I C

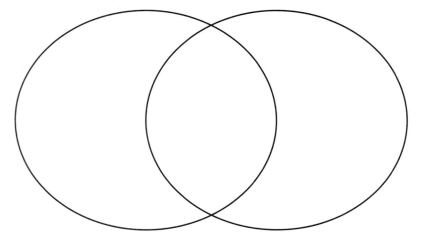

Chapter 8: Vibrations and Waves

Mechanical waves transfer energy through a medium by particle vibration, without altering the medium itself. Sound is a mechanical wave that can travel through a solid, a liquid, or a gas. Sound is a longitudinal wave, so the medium's particles move parallel to the direction of the movement of the sound wave. Sound waves have distinguishing characteristics of shape and time. In terms of shape, a sound wave has amplitude and wavelength. In terms of time, each sound wave has a certain frequency and period. The speed of a sound wave is equal to the product of its wavelength and its frequency. Wave speed is related to the properties of the medium—for example, the temperature of a gas, or the linear density and tension of a string.

Humans can detect sounds over a range of frequencies, loudness, and intensities. We can apply our knowledge of the properties of sound to make work and recreational environments safer.

BIG IDEAS

- Mechanical waves have specific characteristics and predictable properties.
- Sound is a mechanical wave.
- Mechanical waves can affect structures, society, and the environment in positive and negative ways.

Chapter 9: Wave Interactions

When two waves meet, they combine to form a new wave in a process called interference. The amplitudes of the original waves combine according to the principle of superposition: constructive interference results in a wave of greater amplitude, and destructive interference results in a wave of lesser amplitude. When a wave crosses from one medium into another, part of the wave is transmitted and part of the wave is reflected, depending on the medium. Standing waves are a special case of interference between incoming and reflected waves: the resulting wave pattern appears to be stationary. By understanding the properties of standing waves at different frequencies, you can predict the sounds of musical instruments. Wave interactions also help explain other effects; for example, interference between two waves with nearly identical frequencies produces an acoustical beat.

All systems have a certain frequency at which they vibrate most naturally. Wide vibrations at this resonant frequency may result in damage to structures. The Doppler effect describes the change in frequency of a sound when the sound and its observer are moving relative to each other.

Chapter 10: Applications of Waves

Properties of waves help us understand how humans hear sounds and how different instruments produce music. Engineers use wave properties to design structures that have pleasing acoustical qualities, as well as structures that avoid resonance, which can be destructive. Wave characteristics also help explain natural disasters such as earthquakes and tsunamis, and other natural phenomena such as animal communication.

What Is a Vibration?

> **Vocabulary**
>
> vibration   medium   elastic
>
> mechanical wave   net motion   translational molecular motion

MAIN IDEA: A vibration is the cyclical motion of an object about an equilibrium point.

1. Is the following statement true or false? If the statement is false, rewrite it to make it true: A pendulum swings back and forth and returns to rest halfway between the maximum distance it swings to the right and to the left. K/U

2. In the following three descriptions, which phenomenon is a vibration, which is a mechanical wave, and which is neither? Explain. A

    (a) a car's shaking on the highway as a result of an out-of-balance wheel

    (b) a disturbance of water moving away from the point where a rock is dropped into a pool

    (c) a 333 mm bicycle wheel being spun horizontally

MAIN IDEA: All vibrations need a medium to transfer waves.

3. Explain the role that intermolecular forces play as a vibration passes through a medium. K/U

MAIN IDEA: A mechanical wave is a transfer of energy through a medium by particle vibration. Particle vibration is caused by a disturbance to the medium.

4. Which expression describes net motion of a particle over a certain time interval? K/U
    (a) the maximum distance from the starting point during the interval
    (b) the displacement of the particle at the end of the interval
    (c) the sum of the absolute values of the distances travelled during the interval

5. Is the following statement true or false? If the statement is false, rewrite it to make it true: When a wave passes through a medium, all of the particles have changed from their original position. K/U

MAIN IDEA: A medium is a material that permits the transmission of energy due to vibrations. A medium can be a solid, a liquid, or a gas.

6. What properties affect how well a medium transmits vibrations? K/U

7. (a) Define translational molecular motion in your own words.

   (b) Which type of medium—solid, liquid, or gas—relies on translational molecular motion to transfer vibrations? Explain why. K/U

MAIN IDEA: The particles of an elastic medium return to their original location after a wave passes through.

8. Which state of matter is most elastic? Explain your reasoning. K/U

9. Which material would you expect to be more elastic, steel or rubber? Explain your reasoning. K/U A

MAIN IDEA: The speed of a wave and the distance it can travel depend on the composition of the medium. A rigid medium allows a wave to travel longer and faster than a less rigid medium. A less rigid medium disperses more energy, thus reducing the speed and distance that a wave can travel.

10. Use the first column of **Table 1** to arrange the terms *solids*, *liquids*, and *gases* in order of speed of vibration transmission (fastest to slowest). In the second column, explain how characteristics of that row's medium affect the speed of transfer of vibrations. K/U

Table 1 Vibration Transfer in Different Media

Medium	Description of transmission efficiency

STUDY **TIP**

Use a Table
You can use a graphic organizer such as a table to chunk complex material into smaller parts.

11. Draw and label diagrams of particle vibrations in a
    (a) solid   (b) liquid   (c) gas K/U C

Types of Mechanical Waves

Textbook pp. 381–384

> **Vocabulary**
>
> transverse wave   compression   sound
>
> longitudinal wave   rarefaction

MAIN IDEA: In transverse waves, the particles of the medium move perpendicular to the direction of the flow of energy.

1. Illustrate how a transverse wave travels using a series of same-size dots. Include a written description of your diagram. K/U C

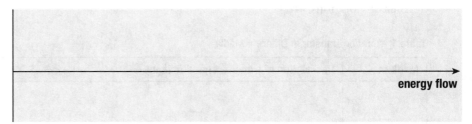

energy flow

MAIN IDEA: In longitudinal waves, the particles of the medium move parallel to the direction of the flow of energy.

2. Illustrate how a longitudinal wave travels using a series of same-size dots. Include a written description of your diagram. K/U C

energy flow

3. Explain how you could send a pulse along a Slinky to create a longitudinal wave. K/U C

MAIN IDEA: In a fluid, longitudinal waves transfer energy through regions of higher and lower pressure. Regions of higher pressure are called compressions. Regions of lower pressure are called rarefactions.

4. (a) Compressions are the regions of a longitudinal wave in which the particles are _____ .
   (b) Rarefactions are the regions of a longitudinal wave in which the particles are _____ . K/U

5. (a) If the particles of a gas are compressed, the pressure is _____ than ambient pressure.
   (b) If particles of a gas are rarified, the pressure is _____ than ambient pressure. K/U

MAIN IDEA: Sound, an important example of a longitudinal wave, is a form of energy produced by rapidly vibrating objects.

6. Sound waves transfer energy through a series of _____ and _____ in the direction of its travel. K/U

7. Our ears detect vibrations that travel through _____ more easily than vibrations that pass through _____ or _____ . K/U

8. Make a tree diagram that shows the relationships between sound waves, longitudinal waves, and mechanical waves. K/U C

MAIN IDEA: Many wave motions in nature are a combination of longitudinal and transverse motion.

9. Explain how the waves on a lake are a combination of longitudinal and transverse motion. K/U C

10. When you hit a nail into a board with a hammer, _____ waves pass through the nail and _____ waves spread out at the surface of the board. K/U

Wave Characteristics

Textbook pp. 385–387

Vocabulary

amplitude	phase	frequency (f)
waveform	phase shift	period (T)
crest	in phase	wave speed (v)
trough	out of phase	simple harmonic motion
wavelength (λ)		

MAIN IDEA: Wave characteristics are based on both wave shape and the behaviour of a wave in time.

1. Refer to **Figure 1** below. Indicate whether each statement is true or false. If the statement is false, rewrite it to make it true. K/U

   (a) The speed of Wave A is twice the speed of Wave B.

   (b) The amplitude of Wave B is half the amplitude of Wave A.

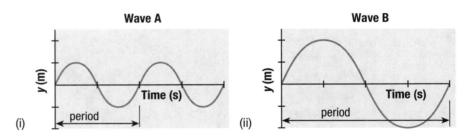

Figure 1

MAIN IDEA: Amplitude is the maximum distance a vibrating particle moves from its equilibrium point.

2. Refer to Figure 1 above. What is the amplitude of Wave A? K/U

3. The amplitude of a _____ wave is measured in metres, while the amplitude of a _____ wave is defined as the difference between the maximum pressure it creates and the pressure of the medium it passes through. K/U

4. (a) Which wave characteristic describes how high a wave is?

   (b) Which wave characteristic describes how fast a wave is moving? T/I

LEARNING **TIP**

Period
The term "period" is also used in other repeating motions, such as revolutions and rotations, to indicate the time for one cycle.

MAIN IDEA: Wavelength is the distance between two similar points in successive identical cycles in a wave, such as from crest to crest or trough to trough.

5. Label the crests and troughs of the wave shown in **Figure 2** below. Use a doubled-ended arrow to indicate the wavelength, λ. K/U C

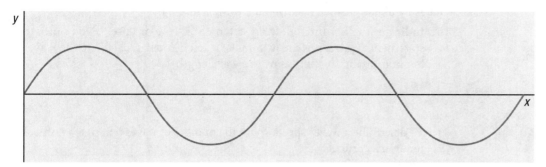

Figure 2

MAIN IDEA: The phase shift is the amount that one waveform is displaced along the *x*-axis from an otherwise identical waveform.

6. The phase shift in **Figure 3** below is _____ the wavelength. K/U

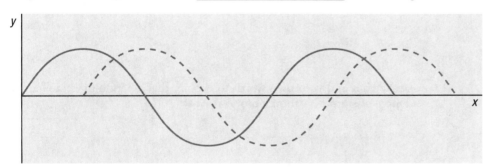

Figure 3

7. When the phase shift between two waves is zero, the two waves are _____. K/U

MAIN IDEA: Frequency is the number of complete cycles of a wave that occur per unit of time (usually 1 s). Period is the time it takes for a vibrating particle to complete one cycle.

8. Determine the frequency and the period of the wave in **Figure 4** below. K/U

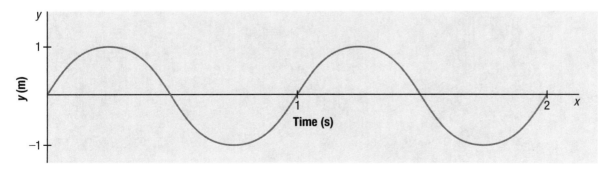

Figure 4

9. (a) The hertz is the SI unit of _____.

    (b) One hertz is equal to _____. K/U

MAIN IDEA: Wave speed is the rate at which a wave travels through a medium. It is also a measure of how fast the energy in the wave is moving.

10. Indicate whether the following statement is true or false. If you think the statement is false, rewrite it to make it true: You can calculate the wave speed by multiplying the period by the wavelength. K/U

11. To determine a wave's speed, count the number of waves that pass a particular point in a particular _____ and _____ by the wavelength. K/U

MAIN IDEA: Simple harmonic motion (SHM) is any oscillating motion that repeats itself at regular intervals.

12. In simple harmonic motion, what can be said about the amplitude, frequency, and period in each cycle? K/U

13. Use sketches and your own words to explain that a pendulum's movement is an example of simple harmonic motion. K/U C

Determining Wave Speed

8.4

Vocabulary

universal wave equation   linear density (μ)

MAIN IDEA: The universal wave equation $v = f\lambda$ relates the speed of a wave to its frequency and wavelength. The universal wave equation applies to all waves.

1. Use the terms *distance*, *time*, and *cycle(s)* to fill in the numerators and denominators. Then simplify to make a true equation:

$$\text{frequency} \times \text{wavelength} = \frac{\text{numerator}_1}{\text{denominator}_1} \times \frac{\text{numerator}_2}{\text{denominator}_2}$$

2. Use the reciprocal relationship between period and frequency to explain that the universal wave equation is equivalent to the kinematics definition of speed. T/I A

> **LEARNING TIP**
>
> **Reciprocal**
> A reciprocal is a number that you can multiply by so that the result equals 1.
> For example, the reciprocal of 4 is $\frac{1}{4}$ because $4 \times \frac{1}{4} = 1$.

3. Use the universal wave equation to complete **Table 1** below. K/U T/I

Table 1 Wavelength, Frequency, Period, and Speed of Waves

λ (m)	f (Hz)	period (s)	v (m/s)
2.0	5.0		
	10.0		50.0
6.0			300
150		1.0	
		0.5	60.0

MAIN IDEA: More rigid intermolecular forces allow for a faster transfer of energy, and therefore a higher wave speed in a medium.

4. If the particles of a medium are connected by strong intermolecular forces, what is the effect on wave speed? K/U

5. Use your sketches in your answer to Section 8.1, Question 11 of the Study Guide to explain why waves can travel more efficiently in a solid than in a liquid or a gas. K/U C

MAIN IDEA: Waves travel faster in hotter gases than in cooler gases because of the increased molecular motion caused by the higher temperature of a hotter gas.

6. Indicate whether the following statements are true or false. If you think the statement is false, rewrite it to make it true. K/U

   (a) Cooler gases are denser than hotter gases, so waves travel faster in cooler gases.

   (b) The speed of sound waves is faster at 40 °C than at 30 °C.

MAIN IDEA: The speed of a wave on a string depends on the linear density of the string and the string's tension: $v = \sqrt{\dfrac{F_T}{\mu}}$.

7. The speed of a sound wave produced by a guitar string will be _____ if the linear density of the string is increased. The linear density can be increased by increasing the string's _____ or by decreasing the string's _____. K/U

8. If the tension on a guitar string is increased, the speed of a sound wave produced by the string will be _____. K/U

Properties of Sound Waves

Textbook pp. 391–397

Vocabulary

audible sound wave	echo	sound intensity
infrasonic wave	Mach number (*M*)	decibel (dB)
ultrasonic wave	pressure (*p*)	

MAIN IDEA: Audible sound waves range from 20 Hz to 20 kHz. Infrasonic waves have frequencies below 20 Hz. Ultrasonic waves have frequencies above 20 kHz.

1. Healthy young adults hear frequencies between 20 cycles per second and
   _____ cycles per second. K/U

2. Earthquake waves are an example of _____ waves that
   have frequencies _____ 20 Hz. K/U

MAIN IDEA: We can apply our understanding of the properties of sound to technologies that benefit society.

3. Describe two applications of ultrasonic waves. K/U

4. (a) What is an echo?

   (b) Explain in your own words how an echo can be used to measure distance. K/U

MAIN IDEA: The speed of sound through the atmosphere, in metres per second, is given by the relationship $v = 331.4 \text{ m/s} + (0.606 \text{ m/s/C}°)T$, where T is the temperature in degrees Celsius.

5. Using the formula relating the speed of a sound wave to the temperature of the air, determine how much the speed of a sound wave changes for a temperature increase of 1 °C. K/U

6. A sound wave is travelling at Mach 2. Explain what this value tells you about the sound wave. K/U

MAIN IDEA: Sound intensity is a measure of the energy flowing through the unit area due to a sound wave. Human hearing can detect a range of sound intensities over many magnitudes in intensity.

7. Indicate whether the following statement is true or false. If you think the statement is false, rewrite it to make it true. The greater the intensity of a sound, the softer the sound. **K/U**

8. The units of measure of sound intensity are _____ per _____. **K/U**

9. In terms of intensity, the range of sounds heard by humans is from about 1×10^{-12} W/m^2 to 1 W/m^2. Explain why it is helpful to use base ten exponents to describe the range. **K/U**

10. Use words or diagrams to explain the relationship between pressure, amplitude, and loudness. **K/U** **C**

MAIN IDEA: Loudness levels are usually described on the decibel scale, which is more convenient than the range of values for sound intensity. Loudness levels are dependent on the distance from the source of the sound.

11. In terms of loudness, what is the range of sounds heard by humans without pain? **K/U**

12. Use **Table 1** below to answer the following questions. **K/U**

Table 1 Loudness as a Function of Distance

Distance (m)	1	10	100	1000	10 000
Loudness (dB)	120	100	80	60	40

(a) Determine the change in perceived loudness when the distance from the sound increases from 1 m to 10 m.

(b) Does each increase in distance by a factor of 10 produce the same change in loudness? Why or why not?

The Sound Barrier

Textbook pp. 398–399

MAIN IDEA: In the late 1940s, the United States and Russia began a weapons race. Competition between the countries stimulated technological advancement.

1. Describe a specific advancement in airplane technology as a result of the arms race. K/U

MAIN IDEA: Shock waves as a plane nears the speed of sound can damage the plane.

2. What is a shock wave? K/U

3. Why is a shock wave hazardous? K/U

MAIN IDEA: The challenge of breaking the sound barrier necessitated developments in plane design and in plane engines.

4. Swept-wing technology allows jet planes to go faster because of the smoother _____ over the _____ wings. K/U

5. Describe the limitations of propeller plane designs and how jet engines overcome these limitations. K/U

MAIN IDEA: A sonic boom occurs when a plane breaks the sound barrier.

6. As a plane reaches the _____, it crashes through the compressions in front of it, releasing enormous amounts of _____ energy. The resulting explosive noise that travels around the plane is known as _____. K/U

7. A sonic boom measures 100 MW/m^2, or 200 db. Why do you think regulations forced commercial aircrafts, such as the SSTs, which could fly faster than the speed of sound, to fly below that speed when they were over land? K/U T/I

MAIN IDEA: Chuck Yeager broke the sound barrier in 1947 at a speed of Mach 1.07.

8. The maximum speed reached by the Bell X–1 was Mach 1.07. Explain the relationship between this Mach value and the speed of sound. K/U T/I

Explore an Issue in Sound

Noise Pollution

MAIN IDEA: Noise pollution affects society and the environment.

1. In your own words, define noise pollution. K/U

2. (a) Describe one reason why the government should get involved in addressing noise pollution.

   (b) Describe one reason why the government should not be involved in noise pollution issues. A

MAIN IDEA: Recommendations for new regulations should be based on research and analysis of alternate solutions.

3. (a) Why is it important to consider the possible impacts of your suggestions?

   (b) Use a tree diagram or other graphic organizer to provide an example of how plans could go wrong when impacts are not considered. C A

Vibrations and Waves

Review what you have learned about vibrations and waves by completing the graphic organizer below. Add your own notes and examples to the graphic organizer to help you study, or create your own graphic organizer.

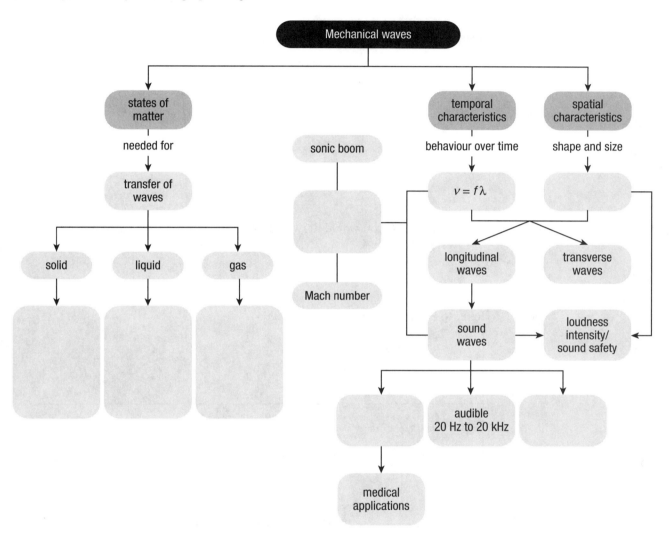

K/U Knowledge/Understanding
T/I Thinking/Investigation
C   Communication
A   Application

1. What is a vibration? (8.1) K/U

2. Explain why a longitudinal wave such as sound is called a compression wave. (8.2) K/U

3. Draw a transverse wave cycle. (8.3) K/U

4. Explain how you would draw a longitudinal wave as if it were a transverse wave. (8.3) K/U

Refer to **Figure 1** to answer Questions 5–7.

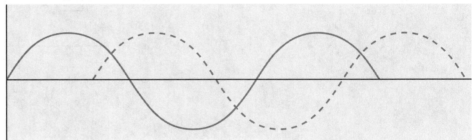

Figure 1

5. Draw arrows to indicate the wavelength, amplitude, and equilibrium point on the graph in Figure 1. (8.3) K/U T/I

6. Explain why you cannot determine the frequency of this wave from the graph. (8.3) K/U

7. What is the phase shift of the dotted wave? (8.3) K/U

8. Make a timeline showing important milestones in the story of breaking the sound barrier. (8.6) **K/U** **C**

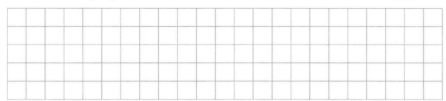

9. A wire of linear density 2.5 g/m is stretched at a tension of 25 N. What is the speed of waves travelling on the wire? (8.4) **T/I**

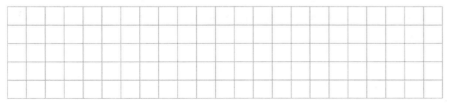

10. Determine if the following statement is true or false. If it is false, rewrite it so that it is true. A motorcycle that makes a sound with intensity 1.0×10^{-3} W/m^2 is 10 times louder than a vacuum cleaner that makes a sound with intensity 1.0×10^{-5} W/m^2. (8.5) **T/I**

11. A flute produces a sound wave that travels at a speed of 333 m/s with a wave length of 1.3 m. Determine the frequency of the wave. (8.4) **A**

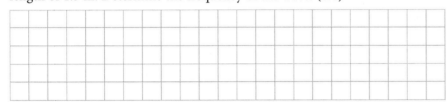

12. Complete **Table 1** to compare the speed of sound in three different locations. Show your calculations in the fourth column. (8.5) **T/I**

Table 1 Speed of Sound at Different Locations

Location	Temperature (°C)	Speed of Sound	Calculation
Mt. Burgess	−35		
Lake Louise	−21		
Banff	−14		

13. Support the importance of addressing the issue of noise pollution in populated areas. Use a graphic organizer to present your argument. (8.7) **C**

Interference of Waves

Textbook pp. 416–419

> **Vocabulary**
>
> interference   constructive interference
>
> principle of superposition   destructive interference

MAIN IDEA: The process of generating a new wave when two or more waves meet is called interference.

1. Briefly outline how water wave particles react when two waves meet each other. K/U

MAIN IDEA: Vibrating particles in a medium react to the sum of all forces on them. Their motion is caused by the sum total of forces on them.

2. Which graphs in **Figure 1** show waves that are in phase? K/U

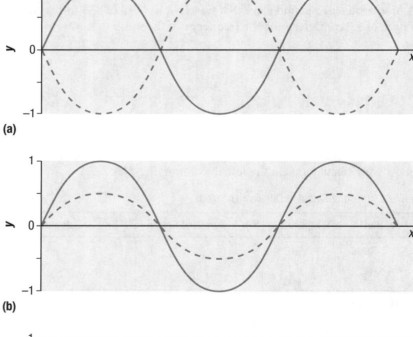

(a)

(b)

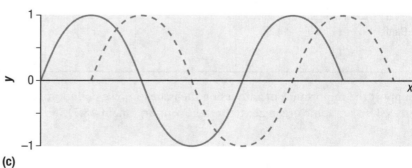

(c)

Figure 1

MAIN IDEA: The principle of superposition states that when two waves meet, the resulting amplitude is the sum of the individual amplitudes.

3. What is the amplitude of the resulting interference pattern of the waves shown in Figure 1(b) on the previous page? K/U

MAIN IDEA: Constructive interference occurs when two waves combine and the amplitude of the resulting wave is greater than the amplitudes of all the individual waves. Destructive interference occurs when two waves combine and the amplitude of the resulting wave is less than at least one of the original amplitudes.

4. Which of the graphs in Figure 1 on the previous page shows only constructive interference? K/U

5. Which of the graphs in Figure 1 on the previous page shows only destructive interference? K/U

6. What interference pattern occurs when two out-of-phase waves meet? K/U

7. (a) Use **Figure 2** below to explain how to apply the principle of superposition to draw the result of two waves overlapping each other.

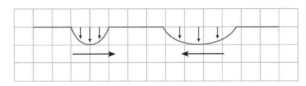

Figure 2

(b) Draw the resultant waveform on the grid. K/U T/I C

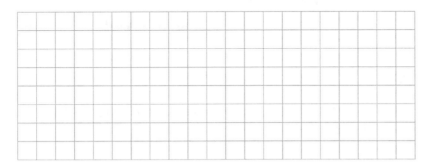

MAIN IDEA: Humans can design technologies to take advantage of wave properties. An example of such a technology is noise-cancelling headphones.

8. Explain how sound-cancelling headphones work. K/U

Waves at Media Boundaries

Textbook pp. 420–426

Vocabulary

media boundary	standing wave	fundamental frequency/ first harmonic (f_0)
free-end reflection	node	harmonics
fixed-end reflection	antinode	overtone
transmission		

MAIN IDEA: The location where two different media meet is called a media boundary. At a media boundary, a wave is partly reflected and partly transmitted.

1. The more similar the two media are, the more energy is _____ .
   The less similar the two media are, the more energy is _____ .
   K/U

2. Give two examples of media boundaries. **K/U**

MAIN IDEA: Free-end reflections produce reflections with the same orientation as the original wave, and fixed-end reflections produce reflections that have the opposite orientation to the original wave.

3. In the diagrams in **Figure 1** below, label the diagram that shows a free-end reflection and the diagram that shows a fixed-end reflection. **K/U**

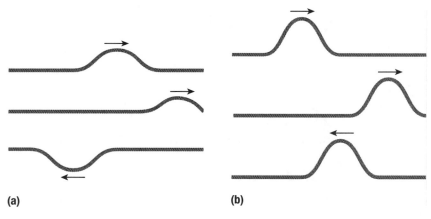

(a)   (b)

Figure 1

4. What would happen to a sound wave as it travels through a metal rod out into the air? Explain your reasoning. **K/U**

5. List examples of a free-end and a fixed-end medium that are not given in your textbook. **K/U**

6. How does a wave behave at media boundary that is neither free nor fixed? K/U

MAIN IDEA: A standing wave is a special case of interference. The waves in a standing wave pattern interfere according to the principle of superposition.

7. When the reflected and the original waves produce a wave pattern that does not appear to move, the resulting wave is called a _____ . K/U

8. Explain what nodes and antinodes of a standing wave are and how they relate to one another. K/U

MAIN IDEA: In cases where a standing wave is produced in a medium that is fixed at both ends or open at both ends, the length of the medium is a whole-number multiple of $\frac{\lambda}{2}$, the first harmonic.

9. Determine if the following statement is true or false. If it is false, rewrite it to make it true. The frequency that produces the simplest standing wave on a medium fixed at both ends is called the medium of the standing wave. K/U

10. (a) Explain why the wavelength of the first harmonic must be twice the length of a medium that is fixed at both ends.

    (b) Express the length of the medium, L, in terms of the fundamental wavelength.

    (c) Explain how subsequent harmonics are related to the first harmonic. K/U

11. Write the sequence of wavelengths that correspond to the first three harmonics in terms of length, L. T/I

12. (a) What is an overtone?

(b) How does an overtone relate to a harmonic? K/U

13. If a wavelength, λ, is 4 m, then the length of the string, L, can be _____ m, _____ m, or _____ m; that is, L_n equals the number n of the harmonic times half the standing wave's wavelength, or $n\frac{\lambda}{2}$>, for n = 1, 2, 3. K/U

MAIN IDEA: In cases of a standing wave that is produced in a medium that is fixed at one end and open at the other end, the length of the medium is determined by $L_n = \frac{(2n - 1)}{4}\lambda$.

14. The speed of a wave on a string, which is fastened at one end, is 350 m/s. The frequency of the wave is 280.0 Hz. What length of string is needed to produce a standing wave with the second harmonic? K/U

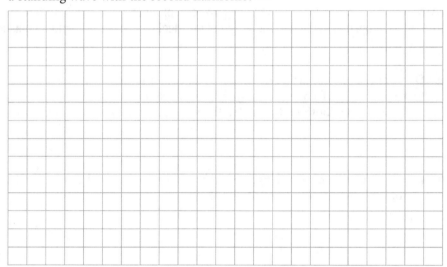

15. The 4th harmonic of a 32 cm violin string is heard. If the speed of sound in the string is 105.5 m/s, what is the frequency of the standing wave? K/U

Beats

Vocabulary

beat   beat frequency

Textbook pp. 427–429

MAIN IDEA: Acoustical beats are an interference pattern formed by two waves with nearly identical frequencies.

1. Determine if the following statement is true or false. If it is false, rewrite it to make it true. Beats are formed when waves with the same amplitude and the same frequencies overlap in the same space. K/U

2. Describe the relationship between the two waves in **Figure 1(a)** at the points corresponding to "B" and "D" in **Figure 1(b)**. K/U T/I

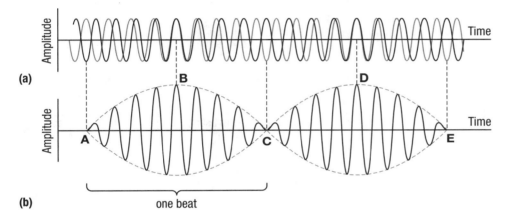

Figure 1

3. Describe the relationship between the two waves in Figure 1(a) at the points corresponding to the nodes in Figure 1(b). K/U T/I

MAIN IDEA: You can hear an acoustical beat as a periodic change in sound intensity.

4. Based on the wave shown in Figure 1(b), identify the points at which the loudest sounds occur. Explain why this is the case. K/U

5. Based on the wave shown in Figure 1(b), identify the points at which you would expect there to be no sound. K/U

MAIN IDEA: Many musical instruments can be tuned by a musician or an instrument tuner by listening to the beats generated between a standard note and that of their instrument.

6. Determine if the following statement is true or false. If it is false, rewrite it to make it true. The beat frequency of the interference pattern generated by two tones of nearby frequencies is defined to be the difference of the two frequencies. K/U

7. Complete the flow chart below to show you can use the concept of "beat" to tune a violin by playing a note on a piano. T/I

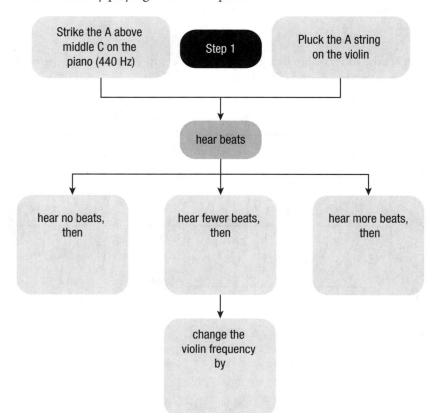

STUDY **TIP**

Use a Flow Chart
You can use a graphic organizer such as a flow chart to track the steps in a process.

Damping and Resonance

Vocabulary

damping   resonant frequency   resonance

MAIN IDEA: Damping is a condition in which the amplitude of a wave is reduced. Either the medium removes energy from a wave, or the effects of destructive interference reduce its amplitude.

1. Draw a dashed-line wave on the graph in **Figure 1** below that shows the effects of damping. K/U T/I

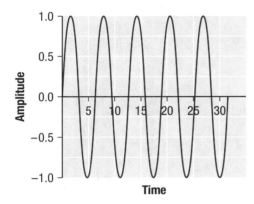

Figure 1

2. Complete the following statements to outline how a child–swing system illustrates damping. K/U

   (a) After one push, a child swings _____ .

   (b) The air _____ the energy provided by the push because of

       _____ and _____ .

   (c) The swing motion narrows and gradually _____ .

MAIN IDEA: Damping due to destructive interference results in little energy loss. Given the right conditions, the amplitude can rapidly increase.

3. In **Figure 2**, how does the wave produced by the interference of multiple waves illustrate the effects of resonance? K/U

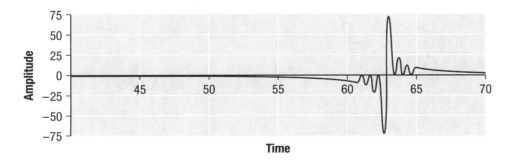

Figure 2

MAIN IDEA: All materials have frequencies at which they vibrate most easily, called the resonant frequency.

4. A violin string's resonant frequency is 196 Hz. What does this tell you about the violin string? K/U

MAIN IDEA: Resonance is the condition in which the frequency of a system equals the wave medium's resonant frequency or one of its harmonics. The wave's amplitude can increase.

5. Explain what happens to a standing wave when the frequency of a wave is not a multiple of one of the harmonics. K/U

6. When is a child–swing system said to be in resonance? K/U

MAIN IDEA: Resonance is avoided in situations such as building construction where vibrations with large amplitudes are undesirable.

7. The Taipei 101 skyscraper is 509.2 m tall from the ground to its highest point. Why would engineers try to prevent resonance? K/U

The Doppler Effect

Textbook pp. 433–435

Vocabulary

Doppler effect

MAIN IDEA: The frequency of a sound wave changes if the source and detector are in relative motion. This phenomenon is called the Doppler effect.

1. Which of the following is true of the Doppler effect? K/U
   (a) This term describes a change in the perceived frequency of a sound.
   (b) This term describes the difference between two observations of sound.
   (c) This term describes the relationship between two sound sources.
   (d) This term describes the relationship between frequency and wavelength of a sound source in motion.

MAIN IDEA: When a source of sound approaches a stationary observer, the observed frequency increases. When the source moves away from a stationary observer, the observed frequency decreases.

2. Draw a diagram showing the changes in frequency and wavelength due to the Doppler effect. K/U T/I C

3. Explain in words the changes in frequency and wavelength due to the Doppler effect. K/U C

MAIN IDEA: The formula used to calculate the change in frequencies detected by an observer as a result of the Doppler effect is $f_{obs} = \left(\dfrac{v_{sound} + v_{detector}}{v_{sound} + v_{source}} \right) f_0$.

4. Suppose a car with a bull-horn megaphone is moving toward a stationary observer on the sidewalk at a speed of 5.0 m/s. The megaphone is broadcasting at a frequency of 100.0 Hz. The speed of sound is 340 m/s. Calculate
   (a) the frequency detected by the observer as the car approaches.

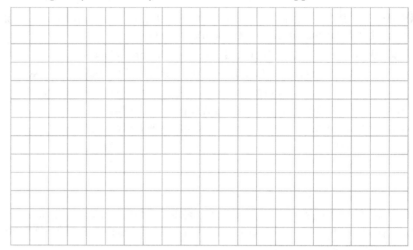

   (b) the frequency detected by the observer after the car passes by. K/U

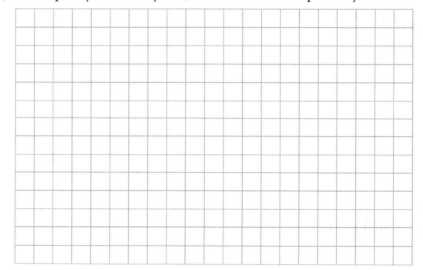

MAIN IDEA: If the source is approaching the detector, the speed of the source is taken to be negative. If the source is receding from the detector, the speed of the source is taken to be positive.

5. In the formula for the Doppler effect, as a sound approaches a detector, the denominator will be _____ than the speed of sound. Therefore, the fraction value is _____ than one, and the product of the fraction value and the observed frequency is _____ than f_0. K/U T/I

6. Assuming the detector is stationary, the velocity of the detector is _____ , so the numerator of the fraction for the Doppler effect equals the _____ . K/U T/I

7. If a sound source approaches an observer at near the speed of sound, the denominator of the fraction approaches _____ , so the fraction value approaches _____ . K/U T/I

Physics JOURNAL

Rogue Waves

MAIN IDEA: A rogue wave is a wave or series of waves that are 50 % to 100 % greater in height than typical for the given wave conditions. Although the reasons rogue waves occur are still not known, the fundamental cause is interference.

1. Use the diagrams in **Figure 1** and **Figure 2** below to provide two different explanations of how rogue waves are caused. K/U C

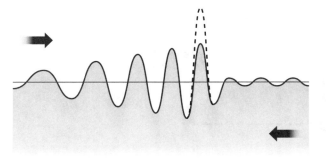
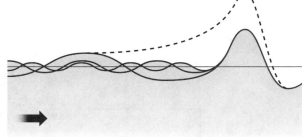

Figure 1

Figure 2

2. What is meant by the "hole in the sea" phenomenon in connection with a rogue wave? K/U

MAIN IDEA: A ship's encounter with rogue waves can result in significant damage.

3. Use the following flow chart to describe what can happen to a ship when it encounters a rogue wave. K/U C

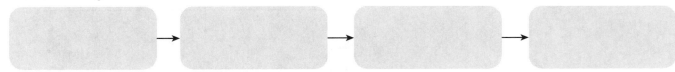

4. In your own words, describe one example of a ship encountering a rogue wave that did not result in a wreck. How was the wreck avoided? K/U C

Wave Interactions

Use the graphic organizer below to review what you have learned about wave interactions. Adding additional notes, diagrams, and explanations to this organizer will help you to create your own study tool for this chapter.

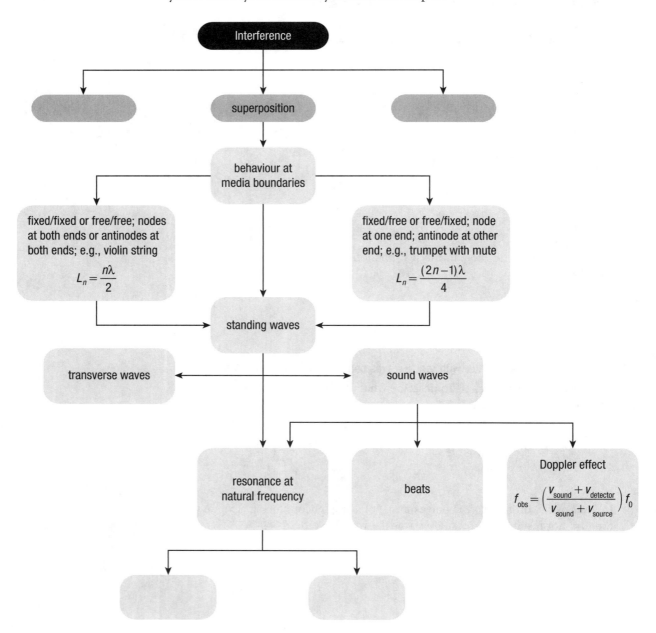

Interference

superposition

behaviour at media boundaries

fixed/fixed or free/free; nodes at both ends or antinodes at both ends; e.g., violin string
$$L_n = \frac{n\lambda}{2}$$

fixed/free or free/fixed; node at one end; antinode at other end; e.g., trumpet with mute
$$L_n = \frac{(2n-1)\lambda}{4}$$

standing waves

transverse waves

sound waves

resonance at natural frequency

beats

Doppler effect
$$f_{obs} = \left(\frac{v_{sound} + v_{detector}}{v_{sound} + v_{source}} \right) f_0$$

1. What happens if a generator first creates a wave at the natural frequency of a wire, and then changes to a frequency lower than that frequency? (9.4) **K/U**
   - (a) At first a standing wave is created; when the frequency is lowered, the nodes of the wave disappear and the standing wave is lost.
   - (b) At first a pulse crosses the wire, and then a smaller pulse is sent back in the reverse direction.
   - (c) At first the wire stays remains in a straight line; when the frequency is lowered, the wire sags in the middle.
   - (d) At first a standing wave is created; when the frequency is lowered, the standing wave's height is reduced.

2. Indicate whether each statement is true or false. If you think the statement is false, rewrite it to make it true. **K/U**
   - (a) When a beat is heard, it is the result of a change in intensity created by interference of two waves of similar wavelengths. (9.3)

   - (b) Although there are several explanatory theories of rogue waves, basically the cause is intensity. (9.6)

3. An inverted triangular wave pulse is travelling toward a rectangular pulse (**Figure 1**). On the blank grid, draw the shape of the resultant pulse when the midpoints coincide. (9.1) **C** **A**

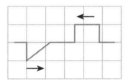 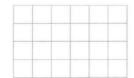

Figure 1

4. A musician plays a tune on a recorder that is 375 mm long. (9.2) **K/U** **T/I**
   - (a) Determine the wavelength for the fundamental harmonic of the recorder.

   - (b) If the musician blows into a glass bottle with a 375 mm air column, is the same fundamental harmonic produced? Why or why not?

5. A 36 cm wire is fastened at both ends. Complete **Table 1** with the wavelengths of the first, second, and third harmonics, and the frequencies corresponding to those wavelengths. Use $v = 324$ m/s as the speed of waves propagated along the wire. (9.2)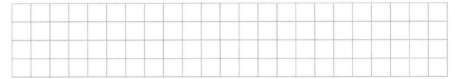

Table 1 Harmonics of a Wire Fastened at Both Ends

		First harmonic	Second harmonic	Third harmonic
(a)	wavelength			
(b)	frequency			

6. If a jet is flying in the direction of an observer at 100.0 m/s, what is the relationship between the frequency of the sound of the jet to the frequency of the observed sound? Assume the speed of sound is 342 m/s. (9.5)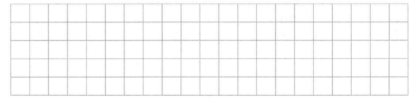

7. (a) If the frequency of a siren is detected at 450.0 Hz as a fire truck approaches an observer, and at 400.0 Hz as the fire truck moves down the road past the observer, determine the speed of the fire truck. Use 342 m/s as the speed of sound.

   (b) Arrange *observed frequency approaching, observed frequency departing,* and *actual frequency* in order from lowest to highest. (9.5) K/U T/I

8. Evaluate the importance of studying rogue waves. Use the Main Idea Web below to organize your thinking. (9.6) C

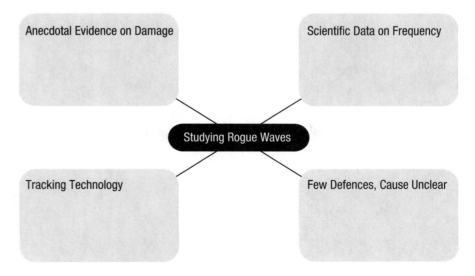

Human Hearing

MAIN IDEA: The characteristics and properties of waves help explain natural phenomena, such as how we hear. The audible human hearing range is from 20 Hz to 20 kHz, but we perceive sound in the frequency range of 1000 Hz to 5500 Hz more than other frequencies.

Textbook pp. 450–453

1. Create a flow chart outlining the process of hearing as sound moves through different parts of the ear. Your chart should summarize the diagram and discussion on page 450 of your textbook. K/U C

STUDY TIP

Flow Chart
You can use a graphic organizer such as a flow chart to track the steps in complex processes.

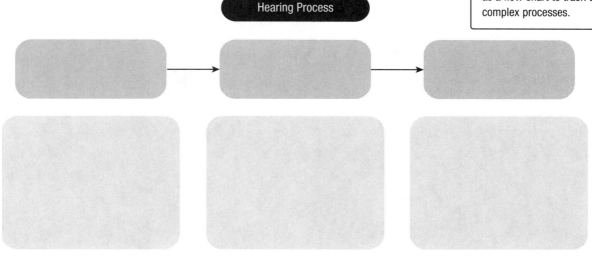

Hearing Process

2. Sound's _____ changes cause _____ in the ear, which are transformed into _____ for the brain to interpret. K/U

3. The auditory canal _____ sounds in the range of 1000 Hz to 5500 Hz by a factor of _____; therefore, we perceive sounds in this range more than other frequencies. K/U

MAIN IDEA: The outer ear consists of the pinna and auditory canal. The pinna gathers sound and channels it into the auditory canal toward the middle ear.

4. On the diagram of the ear in **Figure 1**, label the pinna and the auditory canal. K/U

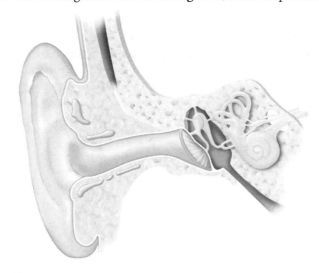

Figure 1

5. Briefly describe the functions of the outer ear. Include functions that are both directly related and not related to hearing sounds. K/U

MAIN IDEA: The middle ear consists of the eardrum and three small bones: the hammer, the anvil, and the stirrup. The eardrum vibrates when it encounters sound waves, and the bones transmit and magnify the vibrations.

6. On the diagram of the ear, shown in **Figure 2**, label the eardrum, hammer, anvil, and stirrup. K/U

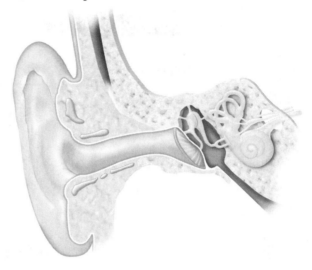

Figure 2

7. The middle ear transmits sound waves in the medium of _____ to the medium of _____ in the inner ear. K/U

8. The _____ pressure of compressions pushes the eardrum _____, and the _____ pressure of rarefactions causes the _____ of air to be pulled away from the eardrum. The resulting vibrations have the same _____ as the sound. K/U

9. Determine if the following statement is true or false. If it is false, rewrite it to make it true. The tiny bones of the middle ear vibrate sympathetically and transmit the vibrations of the eardrum to the oval window of the inner ear. K/U

MAIN IDEA: The inner ear contains the cochlea and the auditory nerve. The vibrations are transformed into electrical impulses in the cochlea. The cochlea sends the impulses through the auditory nerve to the brain.

10. On the diagram of the ear shown in **Figure 3**, label the cochlea and the auditory nerve. K/U

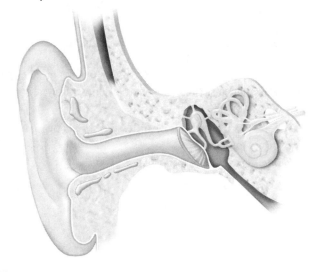

Figure 3

11. Indicate whether the following statement is true or false. If you think the statement is false, rewrite it to make it true: The waves pass hair cells, which vibrate and convert electrical energy into mechanical energy. K/U

12. Summarize what you know about the cochlea. K/U C

MAIN IDEA: Hearing aids can improve hearing loss in some cases.

13. Briefly outline how a typical hearing aid works. K/U

14. What are possible causes of and solutions to loss of hearing due to a damaged ear drum? K/U

Musical Instruments

Vocabulary		
music	pitch	resonator
noise	quality	

MAIN IDEA: Music is a combination of musical notes (standing waves) produced from a source or sources with constant frequencies. Noise is sound produced from a source with constantly changing frequency and amplitude.

1. (a) Refer to **Figure 1** below. Identify which sound wave shows noise and which sound wave shows music.

   (b) Describe the difference between the two types of waves. **K/U**

Figure 1

MAIN IDEA: Pitch, loudness, and quality are three subjective characteristics of sound because they depend on the perception of the listener. Pitch increases when frequency increases. Loudness increases when the amplitude of the sound increases.

2. The loudness of a sound increases when the amplitude of the sound wave increases. Explain why a listener may not perceive the loudness. **K/U**

3. Discuss some factors that influence the perception of music by a listener. **A**

MAIN IDEA: Musical quality depends on the number of harmonics.

4. Distinguish between the quality of a note produced by a tuning fork and that of a note produced by a musical instrument. **K/U**

5. Does the wave in **Figure 2** show a sound with multiple harmonics? Why or why not? K/U

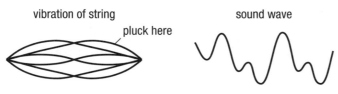

vibration of string

pluck here

sound wave

Figure 2

MAIN IDEA: Musical instruments produce sound with a vibrating source. Most instruments are structured to enhance the sound using resonance.

6. Describe the vibration sources of the three categories of instruments: stringed, wind, and percussion. K/U

MAIN IDEA: Stringed instruments consist of vibrating strings and a resonator, which resonates with the string. The resonator improves the loudness and quality of the sound produced.

7. Explain what a resonator is and what it does. K/U

8. A 0.328 m long violin string vibrates at a fundamental frequency of 659.3 Hz. The violinist pushes the string down, changing the length of the string to 0.308 m. T/I A

(a) What is the fundamental frequency of the shortened string?

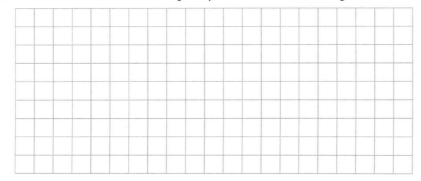

(b) If the string length is shortened, the new fundamental frequency must be higher. Explain.

MAIN IDEA: Wind instruments are composed of open or closed air columns. Vibrations are produced by vibrating lips or vibrating air over the opening of reeds.

9. Determine if the following statement is true or false. If it is false, rewrite it to make it true. Most wind instruments are open air columns. Resonant lengths are directly related to the wave length of the sound in the column.

10. An increase in temperature increases the speed, which changes the _____ and the _____ of a sound wave in an air column. K/U

MAIN IDEA: Percussion instruments produce sound by striking one object against another.

11. Name, describe, and give an example of each of the three categories of percussion instruments. K/U

Acoustics

> **Vocabulary**
>
> building acoustics   reverberation time

Textbook pp. 461–463

MAIN IDEA: The properties of sound influence the design of structures.

1. (a) What is the most important property of sound in the design of a concert hall?

    (b) Explain this property. [K/U]

2. Distinguish between direct sound, early reflections, and later reflections. [K/U]

MAIN IDEA: Building acoustics is the total effect of sound produced in an enclosed or restricted space.

3. Name the two sound phenomena indicated by the arrows in **Figure 1**. [K/U]

Figure 1

4. Explain why the auditorium shown in Figure 1 above demonstrates good acoustical quality. [K/U]

5. The total effect of sound in a room is due in large part to

    _____. [K/U]

MAIN IDEA: Reverberation time is the time for the sound to drop by 60 dB from its maximum intensity or to drop to an inaudible level.

6. In a concert hall, reverberation time should be no more than

    _____. [K/U]

7. How can reverberation time be shortened? [K/U] [T/I]

> **LEARNING TIP**
>
> **Reverberation**
> We say that a strong statement reverberates when it has continuing and lasting effects throughout a group of people or an institution. A room full of people reverberates from the sounds of talking and laughing. The term *reverberation* implies a general bouncing off the walls, while the term *echo* implies a distinct reflected sound.

8. What happens if reverberation time is too long? K/U

MAIN IDEA: The materials, textures, shape, and size of a room are some of the factors that affect a room's acoustics.

9. **Table 1** lists some sound absorption coefficients for several materials. K/U
   (a) Describe the relationship between sound absorption coefficients and reverberation times.

   (b) Describe the relationship between sound absorption coefficients and frequencies.

Table 1 Sound Absorption Coefficients for Various Materials

Material	Frequency (512 Hz)	Frequency (2048 Hz)
concrete	0.025	0.035
wood	0.06	0.10
carpet	0.02	0.27
acoustic tile	0.97	0.68
seated audience	3.0–4.3	3.6–6.0

10. How do the dimensions of a rectangular room relate to sound reflections? K/U T/I

11. Designers try to use _____ rather than curved surfaces to address acoustic issues in rooms. For example, _____ walls tend to concentrate reflected sound waves to a single focal point, while _____ walls tend to _____ sound waves. K/U

12. Create a graphic organizer to summarize the descriptive terms for rooms with different acoustical properties (anechoic, intimate, live, and full). K/U C

Structural Safety

Vocabulary

mechanical resonance   sympathetic vibration   aeroelastic flutter

Textbook pp. 464–465

MAIN IDEA: Mechanical waves can damage structures.

1. What is mechanical resonance? K/U

2. How do mechanical waves damage structures? K/U

MAIN IDEA: Mechanical resonance occurs when a periodic force acts on an object at the natural or resonant frequency of the object. Mechanical resonance must be considered when designing structures and buildings.

3. Explain why when pendulum T begins to vibrate, pendulum P will also start to vibrate (**Figure 1**). K/U

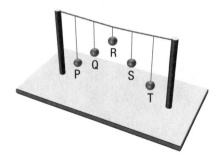

Figure 1

4. Which of the following does *not* describe sympathetic vibration? K/U
   (a) Sympathetic vibration occurs when one object vibrates with another with the same period.
   (b) Sympathetic vibration occurs when window panes rattle at the rumbling of a passing bus.
   (c) Sympathetic vibration occurs when one object vibrates with another at the same frequency.
   (d) Sympathetic vibration occurs when one object vibrates with another object and both objects have the same amplitude.

MAIN IDEA: Aeroelastic flutter occurs when an object is vibrating in air and the input energy is greater than the energy lost due to damping.

5. (a) How are mechanical resonance and aeroelastic flutter similar?

   (b) How are mechanical resonance and aeroelastic flutter different? K/U

6. What are some important lessons to be learned from the collapse of the Tacoma Narrows Bridge? K/U T/I

Seismic Waves

Textbook pp. 466–468

Vocabulary

tsunami   seismic waves

MAIN IDEA: Earthquakes cause different types of waves that move through Earth and across the surface. Underwater earthquakes can cause tsunamis, which can damage coastal land and properties, as well as cause loss of life.

1. Label the P-waves and the S-waves in **Figure 1** below. K/U

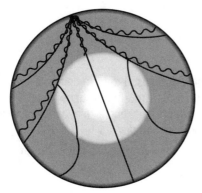

Figure 1

2. Use the graphic organizer below to show how earthquakes result in different types of seismic waves. K/U C

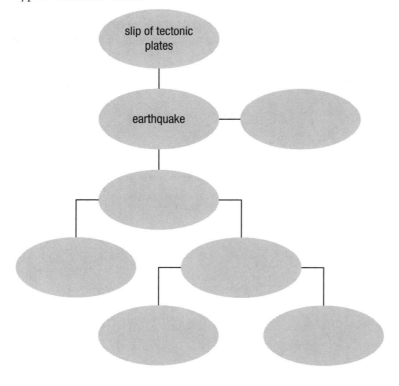

MAIN IDEA: Seismic waves can have a negative impact on society, but technologies can help reduce this impact.

3. Describe some of the negative results of seismic waves. K/U

4. Describe some ways that technology can help reduce the impact of earthquakes. K/U

MAIN IDEA: Seismic geophysical exploration can be used to form computerized images of layers of rock, liquids, and mineral deposits underground and under the ocean floor. These images can be used to determine depth, composition, and size of deposits and where to drill. This method of exploration saves both time and money.

5. What are some of the technological tools used in geophysical exploration? K/U

MAIN IDEA: Similar seismic techniques involving waves have been used to study Earth's interior. Enormous insight has been gained through this method in understanding Earth's interior structure.

6. How are seismic waves used to learn about Earth's interior? K/U

7. What are some of the uses for geophysical exploration? K/U

Vibrations in Aircraft

MAIN IDEA: Properties of mechanical waves influence the design of structures.

Textbook pp. 469–471

1. (a) How do properties of mechanical waves influence the design of structures?

   (b) In particular, how do wave properties influence the design of the wings of commercial aircraft? K/U

MAIN IDEA: Aircraft experience various vibrations. Most vibrations are normal and pose no threat to the operation of the aircraft.

2. Name some common aircraft operations that cause normal vibrations. K/U

3. Describe some normal vibrations related to the body of the aircraft itself. K/U

MAIN IDEA: Aeroelastic flutter is the most dangerous type of abnormal vibration in aircraft, but modern aircraft rarely experience flutter.

4. How are abnormal vibrations identified, and what are some of the causes? K/U

5. Define *buffet* in your own words. K/U

6. _____ is the most dangerous type of vibration. This term is applied to a rapid _____ of the aircraft's _____. The aircraft can fail if the wing flutter has a wide enough _____ and a long enough _____. K/U

7. New aircraft are tested for flutter by pulse and sweep tests. Distinguish between these tests. K/U

Nature and Sound Waves

Textbook pp. 472–474

> **Vocabulary**
>
> echolocation

MAIN IDEA: Natural phenomena can be explained with reference to the characteristics and properties of sound waves.

1. Identify some fundamental tasks that animals accomplish by using sound waves. **K/U**

2. Identify characteristics and behaviours of sound waves that are involved with animals' accomplishment of basic tasks. **K/U**

MAIN IDEA: Dolphins, sperm whales, and orca whales use echolocation to navigate and detect prey in dark, murky waters. Bats also use echolocation to detect prey.

3. Define *echolocation* in your own words. **K/U**

4. Using the flow chart below, show how dolphins detect information about objects in the water at a range of 5 m to 200 m. Between each rectangle and the rectangle beside it, identify the process that goes on between those rectangles. **K/U**

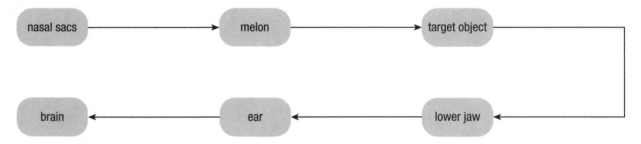

5. Bats create sounds in the larynx that _____ off nearby objects. Sounds are produced at frequencies up to _____ Hz. **K/U**

6. How does a bat detect sound? **K/U**

7. How do bats conserve energy? **K/U**

8. Determine if the following statement is true or false. If it is false, rewrite it to make it true. Bats emit higher-frequency pulses as they approach a target. K/U

MAIN IDEA: Elephants produce infrasound waves, which travel partially through the ground. They can detect these sounds with their feet and trunks pressed against the ground.

9. Elephants produce sounds at _____ frequencies ranging from _____ Hz. K/U

10. Determine if the following statement is true or false. If it is false, rewrite it to make it true. Elephant sounds are as loud as 117 dB, which is softer than human conversations. K/U

11. Determine if the following statement is true or false. If it is false, rewrite it to make it true. Elephant sounds travel up to 10 km and thus elephants can communicate with another herd at a distance. K/U

12. Explain why lifting one foot enables elephants to listen. K/U

MAIN IDEA: Cats use their large movable pinnae to amplify sound and to detect the direction from which sounds are coming.

13. Explain how pinnae help to produce cats' excellent hearing. K/U

14. Complete **Table 1** below. K/U

Table 1 Sound Transmission in Animals

Animal	Method of sound production	Method of sound reception	Frequencies used
dolphin			
bat			
elephant			

Applications of Waves

Complete the following graphic organizer to summarize what you have learned about the applications of waves. At the bottom of the page, create your own study notes or graphic organizer with additional details.

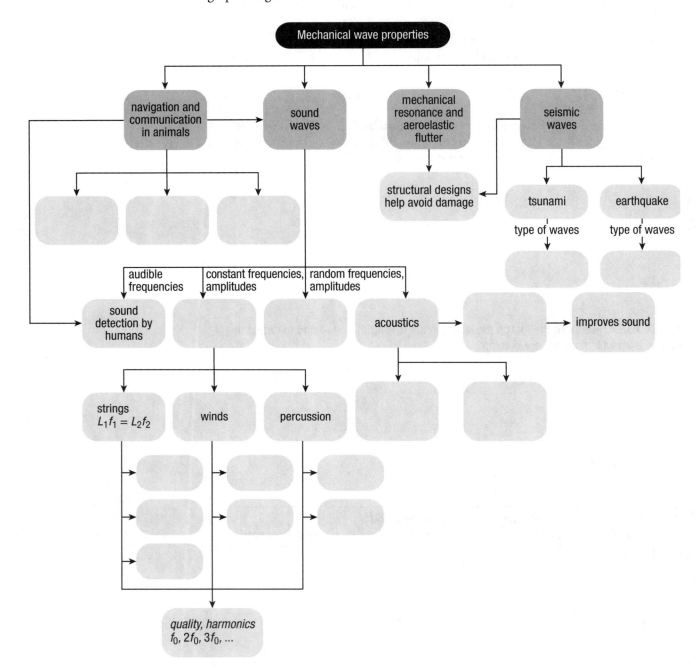

1. Which of the following statements is true about the passage of sound vibrations in the hearing process of humans? (10.1) K/U
   (a) Vibrations pass through the auditory nerve to the ear drum to the cochlea.
   (b) Vibrations pass through the pinna to the middle ear to the auditory canal.
   (c) Vibrations pass from the brain to the middle ear to the pinna.
   (d) Vibrations pass through the auditory canal to the middle ear to the cochlea.

2. If an army is marching, why would the soldiers march out-of-step across a bridge? (10.4) K/U A

3. Seismic waves do not all have the same characteristics. Explain. (10.5) K/U

4. (a) Why do aircraft engineers and pilots worry about aeroelastic flutter?

   (b) How might problems with flutter be addressed by engineers? (10.6) K/U

5. Use a flow chart to explain how bats use echolocation to hunt prey. (10.7) K/U

6. *Computer-generated music* is a term applied to music composed using special software and performed by a computer. Discuss whether this is really music or just noise. (10.2) A

7. A violin string is 32.0 cm long and has a fundamental frequency of 196 Hz. (10.2) K/U T/I
   (a) How long should the string be to produce a frequency of 216 Hz?

K/U Knowledge/Understanding
T/I Thinking/Investigation
C   Communication
A   Application

(b) Compare the wave speeds of the sounds at 196 Hz and at 216 Hz.

8. Bagpipes have three wind components: a chanter, which can produce a melody, and two drones, bass and tenor, which produce single tones. The chanter is tuned to 440 Hz. The tenor drone is tuned to 220 Hz, an octave below the chanter, and the bass is tuned to 110 Hz, an octave below the tenor. The tenor and the bass are tuned to frequencies that are harmonics of the bass's fundamental frequency. Explain. (10.2)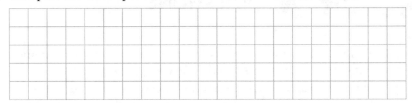

9. Refer to **Figure 1** below to answer the following questions. (10.3)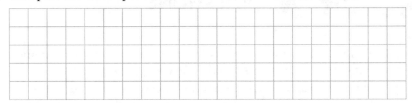

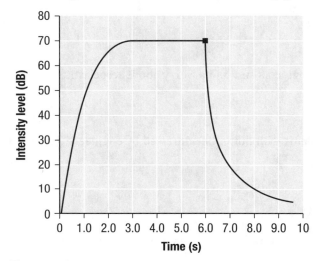

Figure 1

(a) Use the information given in Figure 1 to complete **Table 1** below.

Table 1 Changes to Sound Level v. Time

Time	Effect on sound level
0 s to 3 s	
3 s to 7 s	
7 s to 10 s	
	time for sound to drop from its max level by 60 dB

(b) What is the reverberation time?

1. An extraordinarily large water wave caused by an earthquake is called
   (a) a rogue wave
   (b) a tsunami
   (c) a shock wave
   (d) a P-wave or an S-wave (8.6, 9.6, 10.5) K/U

2. In which part of the human ear are sound waves converted into electrical vibrations? (10.1) K/U
   (a) cochlea
   (b) pinna
   (c) ear drum
   (d) auditory canal

3. Indicate whether each statement is true or false. If you think the statement is false, rewrite it to make it true. K/U T/I
   (a) If the speed of a sound in air is recorded at 340.0 m/s, the air temperature is less than 0°C. (8.5)

   (b) A train whistle has a frequency of 510.0 Hz. After the train passes a person standing by the tracks, the detected frequency is 480.0 Hz. The train is moving at 21.0 m/s. (The speed of sound in this case is 340.0 m/s.) (9.5)

4. List five characteristics of sound waves. (8.1, 8.2) K/U

5. Complete the fishbone diagram on properties of sound waves. (8.3, 8.4, 8.5) K/U

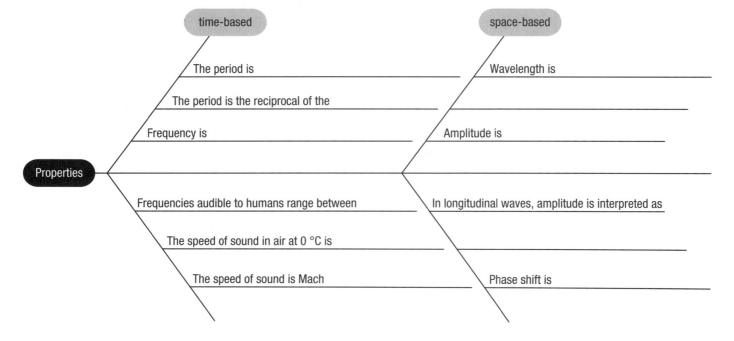

K/U   Knowledge/Understanding
T/I   Thinking/Investigation
C   Communication
A   Application

6. Which wave phenomenon explains the motion of a swing, the destruction of tall buildings, and flutter in planes? (9.4, 10.4) K/U

7. Complete **Table 1** by identifying the interference patterns that are produced when waves with similar characteristics interact. (9.1, 9.3) K/U

Table 1 Wave Interference Patterns

Interfering waves	Produce
identical waves in-phase	
identical waves out-of-phase	
waves with similar frequencies	

8. A wave with a frequency of 60.0 Hz is travelling at a speed of 120.0 m/s on a wire with a mass of 2.5 g. (8.4, 9.2) T/I
    (a) Calculate the wavelength.

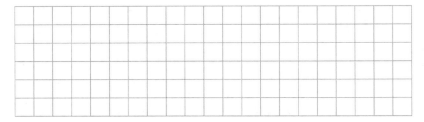

    (b) Calculate the length of the wire.

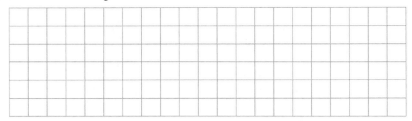

    (c) Calculate the tension of the wire.

9. Determine the first and second harmonic frequencies for a closed-end air column (fixed-free end medium) of length 17 cm. (9.2, 10.2) T/I

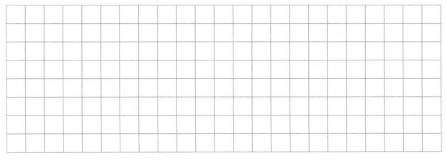

Chapter 11: Electricity and Its Production

Electricity is energy created by the movement of charged particles. In metals, moving free electrons can transfer their energy to different electric devices. Forcing negatively charged electrons close together increases their electric potential. The difference in electric potential between two different points defines a potential difference, or voltage. Ohm's law, Kirchhoff's voltage law, Kirchhoff's current law, and equivalent resistance equations are powerful tools for analyzing electric circuits. The source voltage in a series circuit equals the sum of the voltage drops in the circuit (when current is constant). The source current in a parallel circuit equals the sum of the currents in the parallel paths (when voltage is the same for each parallel path).

Chapter 12: Electromagnetism

Magnetic fields are three-dimensional regions of space that align with Earth's magnetic poles and exert force on magnetic objects. Magnetic field lines never cross. They extend from north to south, and are strongest at poles and in places where lines are closer together. Electric current creates a circular magnetic field around a conductor. The direction of this field is determined using the right-hand rule for straight conductors. Conductors wound in coils create a magnetic field with the same characteristics as a bar magnet. Unlike a bar magnet, the magnetic field of a coiled conductor can be turned off and on by controlling the amount and direction of current. The right-hand rule for solenoids determines the direction of current and magnetic fields for current running in a coil. The right-hand rule for the motor principle provides the direction of fields and currents for motors. Force in a DC motor is kept continuous by the action of a commutator, which reverses the direction of current as the motor runs, keeping it going in the same direction. The development of electric motors has led to thousands of devices powered by electric energy.

Chapter 13: Electromagnetic Induction

A changing magnetic field will induce an electric current. To change a magnetic field, you move the magnet or electromagnet that creates the field, or you fluctuate the current that induces the field. According to Lenz's law, induced current will flow in a direction that creates a magnetic field that opposes the magnetic field that produced the current. Alternating current is created by a conductor loop or armature that is caused by an external force to spin within a magnetic field. Slip rings in the generator allow the current to switch direction every cycle. Transformers raise or lower voltage. Current and voltage in a transformer are inversely proportional to one another. In large power plants, transformers are used to step up voltage and reduce current in order to prevent wasted power.

BIG IDEAS

- Relationships between electricity and magnetism are predictable.
- Electricity and magnetism have many technological applications.
- Technological applications that involve electromagnetism and energy transformations can affect society and the environment in positive and negative ways.

Electrical Energy and Power Plants

Vocabulary

electrical power (*P*)   kilowatt hour (kWh)

MAIN IDEA: Electrical energy is generated from mechanical, thermal, or radiant energy in power plants that operate at various levels of efficiency. Electrical power is the rate at which electrical energy is transformed.

1. The law of conservation of energy states that _____ energy is _____ when energy is transformed from one form to another. **K/U**

2. List two types of power plant technology that transform mechanical energy into electrical energy. **K/U**

3. Which of the following is *not* a unit of power? **K/U**
   (a) watts
   (b) joules per second
   (c) kilowatt hours
   (d) joules per hour

4. Greg transferred 1200 J of energy to his tablet reader in 2.5 min. What power rating does Greg's tablet reader have? **T/I**

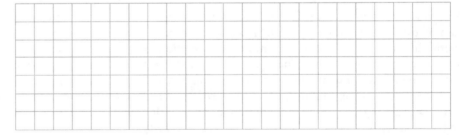

5. A laptop computer is rated at 45 W of power usage. When you plug the laptop in, how much energy will it consume in 3.0 min? **T/I**

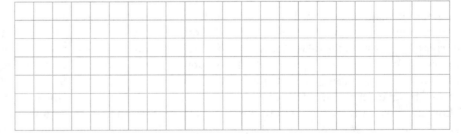

6. An air conditioner has a power rating of 6000 W. What does this power rating tell you about the air conditioner's use of energy? **K/U**
   (a) The air conditioner uses 6000 W of power per second.
   (b) The air conditioner uses 6000 W of electric energy per second.
   (c) The air conditioner uses 6000 J of power per second.
   (d) The air conditioner uses 6000 J of electric energy per second.

7. When she left town, Stephanie accidentally left her 200.0 W television on for an entire weekend from Friday at 6 p.m. to Sunday at 9 p.m. How much energy did Stephanie's television consume

   (a) in kWh?

   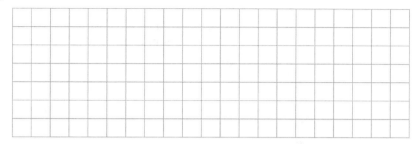

   (b) in joules? [T/I]

8. The energy efficiency of the Huron Wind Farm is 40 %. If its turbines take in 2.7 million joules in the form of mechanical energy, how much electrical energy would you expect them to generate in 1 kWh? [T/I]

9. Power ratings for common household appliances are given in **Table 1**. [K/U] [T/I] [C] [A]

   (a) Estimate the time your household uses each appliance each day, and record these values in **Table 1**. Then calculate the amount of energy each appliance uses. Record your answers in **Table 1**.

Table 1 Electrical Energy Used by Various Appliances

Appliance	Power rating (W)	Time used per day	Electrical energy used per day (kWh)
dishwasher	1200.0		
toaster	1000.0		
television	220.0		
air conditioner	7000.0		
laptop	50.0		
refrigerator	600.0		
Total energy used in one day			

(b) Rank the appliances with respect to energy used per day from greatest to least.

(c) What percent of the total energy used in a day is consumed by the device that consumes the greatest amount of energy? the least amount of energy?

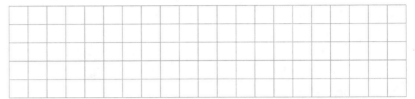

(d) If you were going to reduce the use of one appliance in your home to save money on electrical bills, which appliance would you choose? Explain.

10. A compact fluorescent bulb emits the equivalent of 40 W of light but is rated at only 11 W. Using the compact fluorescent bulb for a full 24 h uses the same amount of energy as burning a conventional 40 W incandescent bulb for how many hours? T/I A

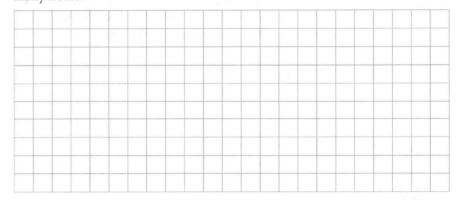

MAIN IDEA: Power plant technologies vary in efficiency, and each technology has impacts on the environment and society.

11. A politician who lives in a windy area proposes that her region get rid of all power plants and use wind farms exclusively to generate power. What is the flaw in her proposal? Explain. T/I C

12. A power plant is 45 % efficient, meaning that more than half of the plant's input energy is "lost" and does not generate electric power. Is this "lost energy" a violation of the law of conservation of energy? Explain. K/U C

Clean Coal Technology

1. Carbon capture technologies first _____ carbon dioxide, then store it deep underground or dissolved in the oceans as a _____. K/U

2. Complete **Table 1** for the stakeholders in this activity. A

Table 1 Stakeholder Motivations

Stakeholder	Likely to favour upgrading or investing in alternative methods?	Reason
power plant executive		
clean coal technology manufacturer		
environmentalist		
government minister		
alternative power plant executive		
community member		

> **LEARNING TIP**
>
> **Combustion and Greenhouse Gases**
> Keep in mind that all forms of energy production that feature combustion generate greenhouse gases.

3. Explain how the answer to each of the following questions can help you make a decision about whether to recommend upgrading the coal-fired plant or investing in alternative methods of power generation. K/U C A

   (a) With respect to costs, how do clean coal plants compare to alternative power plants?

   (b) How do clean coal plants compare to alternative energy plants with respect to
       (i) jobs?
       (ii) impact on habitats?
       (iii) pollution?

Electric Potential Difference

Textbook pp. 510–513

Vocabulary

electric potential   electric potential difference (*V*)   voltmeter

---

LEARNING TIP

Measuring Potential Difference
Remember that potential difference always must be measured between two different locations.

MAIN IDEA: Electric potential difference is a measure of how much electric potential energy is associated with charges. Electric potential difference, or voltage, is the difference in electric potential energy of the charges (electrons) between two points in a circuit.

1. What property of metal allows it to transfer electrical energy? **K/U**

2. Pushing electrons _____ the potential energy they have; resulting in an increase in _____. **K/U**
   (a) closer together increases, voltage
   (b) closer together decreases, charge
   (c) farther apart increases, voltage
   (d) farther apart decreases, charge

3. Is the following statement true or false? If you think the statement is false, rewrite it to make it true: Electric potential is a measure of potential energy at a single location, while electric potential difference compares the difference in potential energy between two locations. **K/U**

4. In order to measure the voltage of a circuit accurately, a voltmeter must be connected _____ the loads in the circuit. **K/U**
   (a) in series with
   (b) in parallel with
   (c) before
   (d) after

5. Use the following terms to complete the Venn diagram below. **K/U** **C**

   - joules/coulomb
   - can be measured in volts
   - measured at one point in circuit
   - measured at two points in circuit
   - amount of potential energy at a single location

   - change of potential energy between different locations
   - commonly referred to as voltage
   - measure of potential energy
   - $V = \dfrac{\Delta E}{Q}$

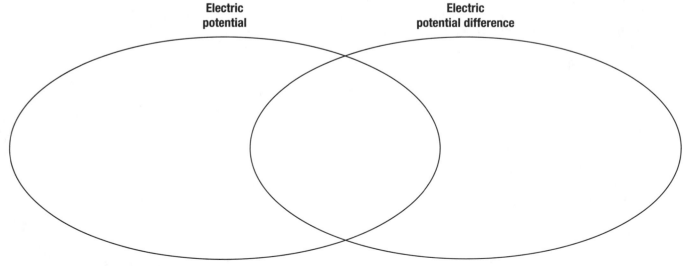

Electric potential   Electric potential difference

MAIN IDEA: Electric potential difference is measured in volts and calculated using the equation $V = \dfrac{\Delta E}{Q}$, where V is the electric potential difference in volts, ΔE is an energy change, and Q stands for the charge or number of electrons that are flowing in coulombs (C).

6. When you push a certain doorbell button, 1204 J of electric potential energy is transformed into electrical energy that produces sound, moving 86 C of charge in the circuit. What is the electric potential difference between the terminals of the doorbell circuit? T/I

7. A circuit includes a light bulb and a power source. **Figure 1** shows different ways to measure the voltage of the circuit using a voltmeter. Which diagram in **Figure 1** shows the proper way to measure the voltage? Explain. T/I C

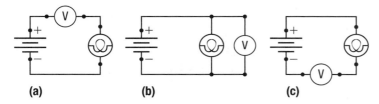

(a)   (b)   (c)

Figure 1

8. A 12 V car battery puts out 5400 J of energy each second. How many coulombs of charge does this battery put out in one second? T/I

MAIN IDEA: Sources of electrical energy cause an increase in the electric potential (voltage gain), whereas loads cause a decrease in the electric potential (voltage drop).

9. Two batteries have the same voltage. Battery A supplies twice as much energy per second as battery B. How is this possible? Explain. K/U T/I C

10. A power source puts out 10 V. A voltmeter is used to measure voltage at points A, B, and C in **Figure 2**. T/I

    (a) At which point in the circuit will the voltage have the greatest value?

    (b) At which point in the circuit will the voltage have the lowest value?

    (c) At which point in the circuit will the voltage have an intermediate value between the other extremes?

    (d) At which point in the circuit will the electrons be closest together? At which point will they be farthest apart? Explain.

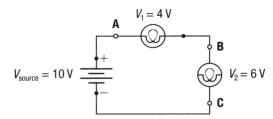

Figure 2

11. Explain how increasing the voltage in a circuit increases the potential energy of the electrons that flow in the circuit. C A

12. Marvin is setting up the equipment for his rock band. He hooked up his amplifier to a 110 V power source using a thin cable that was 20 m in length. Using a voltmeter, Marvin found that the voltage going into the amplifier was considerably less than 110 V. How do you explain the drop in voltage? C A

Physics JOURNAL

Is Benjamin Franklin to Blame?

Textbook pp. 514–515

MAIN IDEA: The reason that conventional current is defined as the direction in which positive charges flow dates back to experiments by Benjamin Franklin in the eighteenth century.

1. What did Franklin's famous kite experiment prove? K/U
   (a) Lightning is a form of electricity.
   (b) Electricity can be safely stored in a Leyden jar.
   (c) Lightning is a form of negative electricity.
   (d) Lightning has both negative and positive forms.

2. In Franklin's view, any material that obtained an excess of electricity by rubbing it on another material was identified as _____ in charge. K/U

3. Franklin saw that a charged piece of amber and a charged piece of glass attracted one another. What can you conclude from this result? K/U

4. Franklin made the determination that glass has an "excess of electricity" and is therefore positive in charge. Complete **Table 1** below using the same logic that Franklin might have used. T/I A

Table 1 Behaviour of Materials in Response to Amber and Glass

Material	Excess or deficit of electricity?	Response to amber	Response to glass	Charge
glass	excess	attract	repel	positive
amber		repel	attract	
fur		attract	repel	
silk		repel	attract	

5. (a) Explain what Franklin's "mistake" was.

   (b) How was Franklin's mistake discovered?

   (c) Explain why scientists do not correct the mistake that Franklin made. K/U C

Electric Current

> **Vocabulary**
>
> direct current (DC)   ammeter

LEARNING TIP

Amperes and Coulombs
Current is measured in amperes, and charge is measured in coulombs.

MAIN IDEA: Direct current is a measure of the number of electrons flowing in one direction only.

1. Direct current, in the form of _____, flows from the _____ terminal of a power source to the _____ terminal. K/U

2. On **Figure 1**, draw the direction that conventional current would flow and the direction that electrons would flow. Label your diagram. K/U A

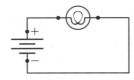

Figure 1

3. Which statement is true of direct current flowing in a conductor? K/U
   (a) The free electrons move through the wire, but the conductor atom nuclei stay in place.
   (b) Both the free electrons and the conductor atom nuclei move through the wire.
   (c) Neither the free electrons nor the conductor atom nuclei move through the wire.
   (d) The conductor atom nuclei move through the wire, but the free electrons stay in place.

MAIN IDEA: Direct current is measured in units of amperes (coulombs per second).

4. Is the following statement true or false? If you think the statement is false, rewrite it to make it true: Only a very small number of electrons move along a wire that has a current of 1 A. K/U

5. To measure current accurately, an ammeter must be connected _____ with a circuit. K/U

6. A current of 4.6 A moved through a wire for 3.5 s. How many coulombs of charge flowed through this wire? T/I

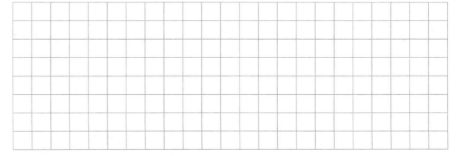

7. A total charge of 0.060 mC flowed through a wire for 2.4 s. What was the current in this wire? Answer in microamperes. T/I

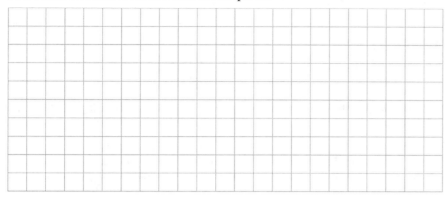

8. A circuit includes a light bulb and a power source. Draw a circuit diagram to show how you would connect an ammeter to accurately measure current in the circuit. C

9. Is the following statement true or false? If you think the statement is false, rewrite it to make it true: The electrons in a current of 2 A are moving at the same speed as the electrons in a current of 1 A. T/I

10. A charger for an electric shaver needs 2.7 C of electrons to fully charge the device with a current of 0.6 mA. How long does it take to charge the shaver? T/I

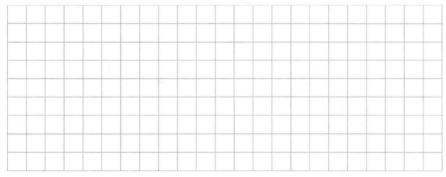

11. In a wire, 0.8 C of electric charge passes through a point in 1.2 min. Is this current strong enough to harm a human being? Explain. A

12. A large 12 V automobile battery can produce powerful shocks that can harm a human being. A small battery used for electronic devices also produces 12 V, but it does not produce dangerous shocks. Explain. C A

Kirchhoff's Laws

> **Vocabulary**
>
> Kirchhoff's voltage law (KVL) Kirchhoff's current law (KCL)

MAIN IDEA: Kirchhoff's laws define the relationships between voltage and current in an electric circuit.

> **LEARNING TIP**
>
> **Remembering KVL and KCL**
> For a series circuit, voltages add up and currents remain constant. For a parallel circuit, voltages remain constant and currents add up.

1. Is the following statement true or false? If you think the statement is false, rewrite it to make it true: Kirchhoff's voltage law states that the sum of the electric potentials across loads in the circuit is equal to the electric potential at the source. K/U

2. A series circuit has three loads and a source voltage of 24 V. Which of the following statements is true? K/U
   (a) Each load in the circuit must be 8 V.
   (b) Each load in the circuit must be 24 V.
   (c) The sum of the loads in the circuit must equal 24 V.
   (d) The sum of the loads in the circuit must be zero.

3. A parallel circuit has two separate parallel paths and a source voltage of 12 V. Which of the following statements is true? K/U
   (a) Each load in the circuit must be 12 V.
   (b) Each path in the circuit must have a voltage of 12 V.
   (c) The sum of the loads in the circuit must equal 24 V.
   (d) The sum of the loads in the circuit must be zero.

4. Complete **Table 1** for Kirchhoff's laws. K/U

   Table 1 Comparing Kirchhoff's Laws

		Series	**Parallel**
(a)	**Kirchhoff's current law**	$I_{series} =$	$I_{parallel} =$
(b)	**Kirchhoff's voltage law**	$V_{series} =$	$V_{parallel} =$

MAIN IDEA: Kirchhoff's laws of voltage and current can be used to solve problems with mixed circuits.

5. In **Figure 1** below, the source voltage is 30.0 V, V_1 is 18 V, and V_4 is 8.0 V. T/I

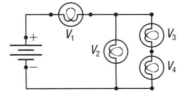

Figure 1

(a) What is the value of V_2?

(b) Which is greater, V_2 or the combined voltage of V_3 and V_4?

(c) What is the value of V_3?

6. In **Figure 2** below, I_1 is 0.60 A and I_4 is 0.25 A. T/I

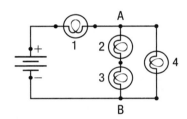

Figure 2

(a) What is the value of the source current?

(b) Which current is greater, I_2 or I_3? Explain.

(c) Which current is greater, I_1 or I_2? Explain.

(d) What is the value of I_2?

(e) What is the value of I_3?

(f) What is the value of the current at points A and B? Explain.

7. In **Figure 3**, $V_1 = 10.0$ V, $V_4 = 30.0$ V, $I_1 = 0.500$ A, $I_4 = 0.100$ A, $V_3 = 20.0$ V, and $I_3 = 0.300$ A. T/I

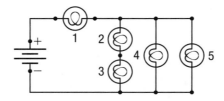

Figure 3

(a) What is the value of V_5?

(b) If $V_3 = 20.0$ V, what is the value of V_2?

(c) What is the value of I_5?

(d) What is the value of I_2?

Electrical Resistance

Vocabulary			
electrical resistance (*R*)	resistor	Ohm's law	ohmmeter

Textbook pp. 523–526

MAIN IDEA: Electrical resistance is a measure of how difficult it is for current to pass through a material.

1. Materials such as plastic and rubber are good insulators because they have _____ resistance. **K/U**

2. Is the following statement true or false? If you think the statement is false, rewrite it to make it true: A material with high electrical resistance will also have high conductance. **K/U**

3. A car needs a large amount of current from its battery to start on a cold day. In order to deliver this current, car designers are likely to choose wires that are
    (a) high in resistance
    (b) low in resistance
    (c) low in conductance
    (d) high in both conductance and resistance **K/U**

4. Georg Simon Ohm conducted several experiments in which he measured the current and voltage in circuits. What did he find? **K/U**
    (a) As voltage increased, current increased by a constant amount that Ohm identified as resistance.
    (b) As voltage increased, current decreased by a constant amount that Ohm identified as resistance.
    (c) As voltage decreased, current increased by a constant amount that Ohm identified as resistance.
    (d) As voltage increased, resistance increased by a constant amount that Ohm identified as current.

5. Is the following statement true or false? If you think the statement is false, rewrite it to make it true: All materials have at least some resistance, which turns electrical energy into thermal energy when a current passes through them. **K/U**

6. When using a(n) _____ to measure resistance, turn off the power supply and make sure the device is connected in _____ with the circuit. **K/U**

7. What is the resistance of a device that has a current of 2.5 A and a voltage of 240 V? **T/I**

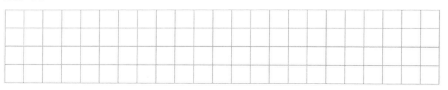

> **LEARNING TIP**
>
> **Remembering Ohm's Law**
> The equation for Ohm's law can be rewritten as *V* = *IR*, which is easier to remember if you use a mnemonic: *VIR* = Very Important Resistance.

8. How could you use a voltmeter and an ammeter to find the resistance of a resistor in a circuit? [C] [A]

9. An engineer is designing an electric heater with an element that heats up as current passes through it. What resistance quality should the heating element have: high, low, or medium? Explain. [K/U] [C]

10. Graphs of voltage versus current are shown in **Figure 1**. [C] [A]

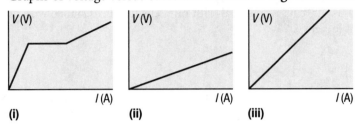

(i)   (ii)   (iii)

Figure 1

(a) Which graph shows a resistor with the greatest resistance? Explain how you know.

(b) Which graph shows a resistor with variable resistance? Explain how you know.

11. Look at the graph in **Figure 2** below. [C] [A]

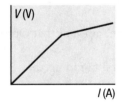

Figure 2

(a) How would you characterize the relationship between voltage and resistance for the graph?

(b) In the space provided, show a graph of a variable resistor that has low resistance at low voltages, and smoothly increases resistance as voltage increases.

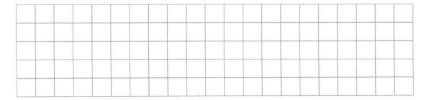

Resistors in Circuits

Vocabulary

equivalent resistance

Textbook pp. 527–530

MAIN IDEA: Connecting resistors in series and in parallel to existing circuits changes the total resistance and current through the circuits in predictable ways.

1. Adding an extra resistor to a circuit in series will decrease the _____ across each resistor. K/U

2. Adding an extra resistor in parallel to a circuit will _____ the current in the circuit. K/U

3. Is the following statement true or false? If you think the statement is false, rewrite it to make it true: Adding a resistor to a series circuit increases the total resistance of the entire circuit. K/U

4. Is the following statement true or false? If you think the statement is false, rewrite it to make it true: Adding a resistor in parallel to a circuit increases the total resistance of the entire circuit. K/U

> **LEARNING TIP**
>
> **Equivalent Resistance in a Parallel Circuit**
> For a parallel circuit, the equivalent resistance is always less than the least resistance in the circuit.

5. Consider circuit A shown in **Figure 1** below.

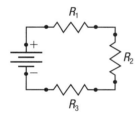

Figure 1

(a) Express the total voltage drop in the circuit using Ohm's law. T/I

(b) Show how you can use the equation you wrote in (a) to write an equation for the total resistance of the circuit. T/I

(c) If $R_1 = 12\ \Omega$, $R_2 = 8.0\ \Omega$, and $R_{total} = 34\ \Omega$, determine the value of R_3. T/I

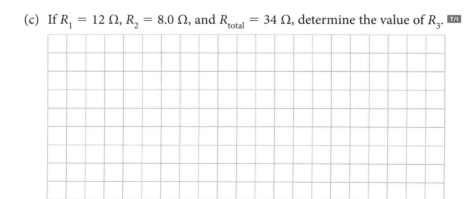

(d) Draw an equivalent circuit for circuit A. [C]

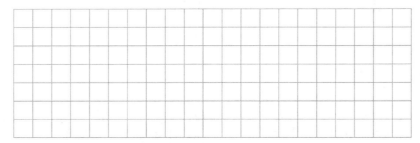

6. A resistor R_4 is added to circuit A to create circuit B as shown in **Figure 2**. Which of the following will occur as a result of inserting R_4? [K/U]

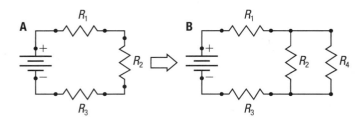

Figure 2

(a) The total resistance of the circuit will increase.
(b) The total resistance of the circuit will decrease.
(c) The resistance of R_1 will decrease.
(d) The resistance of R_1 will increase.

7. As a result of inserting R_4 in circuit B shown in Figure 2 above, how will the current in the circuit change? [T/I]
(a) The current through R_1 will increase.
(b) The current through R_3 will increase.
(c) The current through R_2 will increase.
(d) The current through R_2 will decrease.

8. For circuit A shown in **Figure 3**, $R_1 = 9.0\ \Omega$, $R_2 = 12.00\ \Omega$, and $R_3 = 8.00\ \Omega$. Circuit B is identical to circuit A, but an extra resistor, R_4, has been inserted. [T/I] [C]

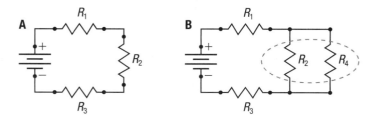

Figure 3

(a) What is the total resistance of circuit A?

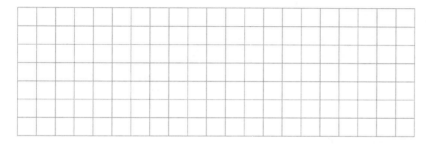

(b) If $R_4 = 10.00 \ \Omega$, what is the equivalent resistance of the parallel part of circuit B, which includes R_2 and R_4? (See the circled area in Figure 3.)

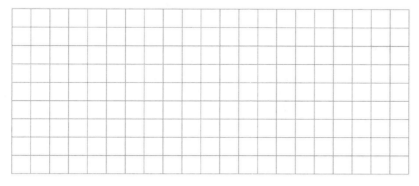

(c) Redraw circuit B to create a new circuit using the equivalent resistance you calculated in (b).

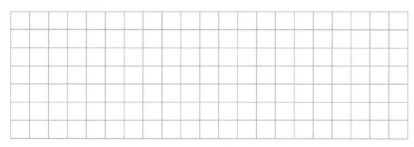

(d) Compare the total resistance of circuit C to circuit A. What do you conclude?

Circuit Analysis

MAIN IDEA: Ohm's laws, Kirchhoff's laws, and equivalent resistance can be used to solve problems that involve complex mixed circuits.

Textbook pp. 531–535

1. In the circuit shown in **Figure 1**, the source current is 0.9 A, $R_1 = 10.0\ \Omega$, $R_2 = 6.0\ \Omega$, $R_3 = 12.0\ \Omega$, and $I_2 = 0.6$ A.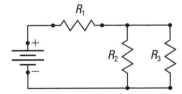

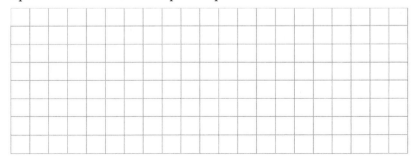

Figure 1

(a) What is the value of $R_{parallel}$, the equivalent resistance for the parallel path?

(b) Draw an equivalent circuit for the circuit shown in **Figure 1** showing an equivalent resistance for the parallel path. Label each resistance.

(c) Determine the source voltage of the circuit.

(d) Determine the value of I_3.

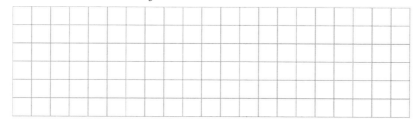

2. In the diagram shown in **Figure 2**, the source voltage is 30.00 V, R_1 = 10.00 Ω, R_2 = 18.00 Ω, R_3 = 12.00 Ω, R_4 = 32.80 Ω. Use the circuit to solve the problems below. **T/I**

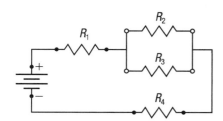

Figure 2

(a) Determine the total resistance of the circuit.

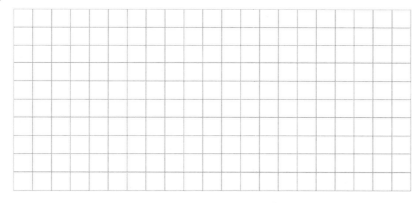

(b) Calculate I_{source} using Ohm's law.

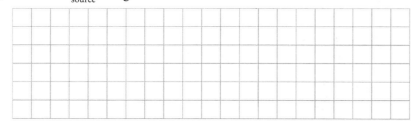

(c) Calculate V_1 and V_4 using Ohm's law.

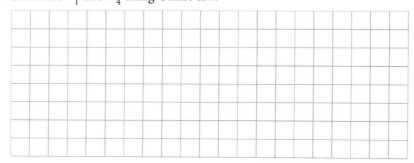

(d) Determine $V_{parallel}$, the potential difference across the parallel part of the circuit.

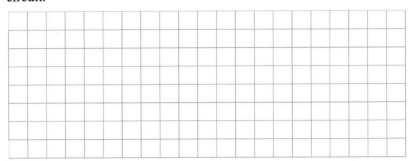

(e) Determine V_2 and V_3, the potential difference across both R_2 and R_3.

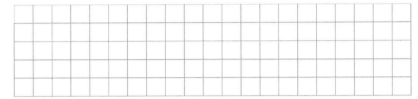

(f) Calculate I_2 and I_3 using Ohm's law.

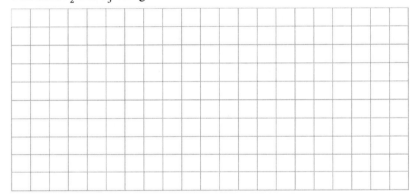

3. Use the values you calculated from Question 2 above to write in values for each point on the circuit in **Figure 3** and **Figure 4**. T/I C

   (a) Label the values for potential difference across R_1, R_2, R_3, R_4, and the power source.

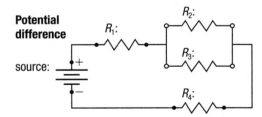

Figure 3

   (b) What is the total voltage drop for the circuit? How is the total related to the source voltage? Explain.

(c) Label the values for current through R_1, R_2, R_3, R_4, and the power source in **Figure 4**.

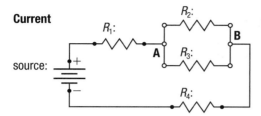

Figure 4

(d) How does the current entering point A at the parallel part of the circuit compare to the source current? Explain.

(e) If R_1 is 12 Ω, R_2 is 8 Ω, and R_{total} is 34 Ω, calculate the value of R_3.

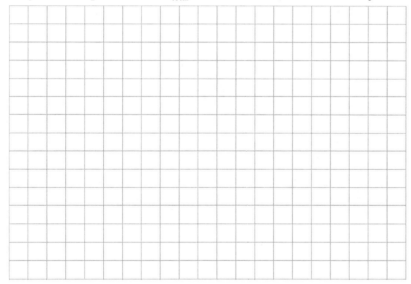

(f) Draw an equivalent circuit for the circuit shown in **Figure 3** and **Figure 4** above.

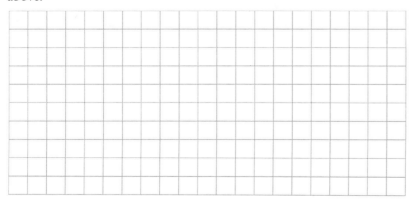

Electricity and Its Production

Complete the graphic organizer below to summarize what you have learned about electricity and its production. Add your own notes and examples to help you study the concepts from Chapter 11.

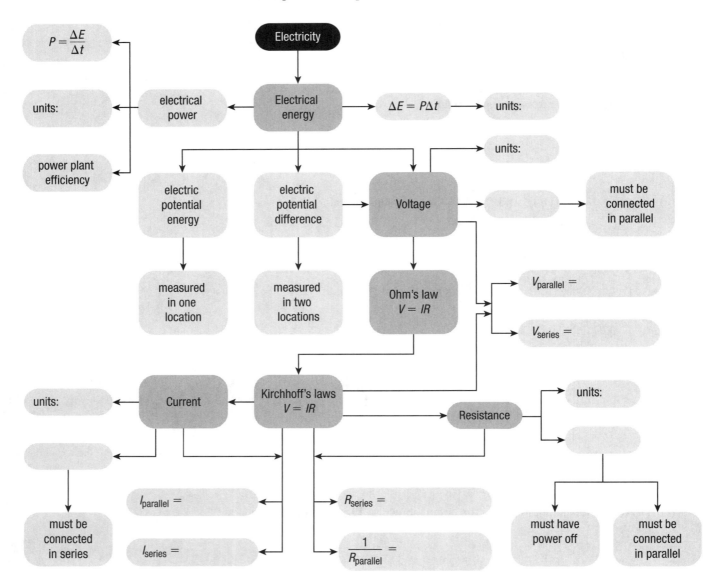

1. Kilowatt hours are units of electrical _____. (11.1) **K/U**

2. Since electrons repel one another, pushing electrons closer together increases the amount of _____ energy they have. This energy is measured in joules per coulomb, or _____. (11.3) **K/U**

3. More complete combustion of coal involves turning coal to hydrogen and carbon monoxide gases and burning the gases in a process called _____. (11.2) **K/U**

4. An ammeter must be set up in _____ with a circuit, while a voltmeter must be set up in _____. (11.3, 11.5) **K/U**

5. Franklin's "mistake" was that he identified charges that moved from one substance to another as _____. (11.4) **K/U**

6. Which of the following statements is true? (11.6) **K/U**
   (a) In a parallel circuit, V_{source} is equal to the sum of voltages in the circuit.
   (b) In a series circuit, I_{source} is equal to the sum of currents in the circuit.
   (c) In a series circuit, all voltages are equal to the source voltage.
   (d) In a parallel circuit, all currents are equal to the source current.

7. A light bulb burned 210 000 J of energy in 28 min. What power rating does the light bulb have? (11.1) **T/I**

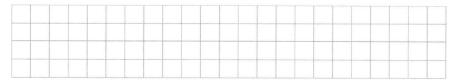

8. A battery-powered heater moves 64 C of charge per second that require 1536 J of energy. What is the voltage of the heater? (11.3) **T/I**

9. A device requires 1.8 C of electrons to be fully charged. The device's charger delivers charge at a rate of 0.36 mA. How long does it take to fully charge the device? (11.5) **T/I**

10. In **Figure 1**, $V_1 = 25$ V, $V_{source} = 50.0$ V, $V_4 = 10.0$ V, $I_1 = 1.0$ A, and $I_2 = 0.60$ A. (11.6) **T/I**

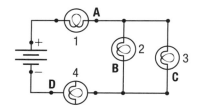

Figure 1

K/U Knowledge/Understanding
T/I Thinking/Investigation
C Communication
A Application

(a) What is the value of V_2?

(b) What is the value of V_3?

(c) At which point or points in the circuit will the ammeter have a reading that is lower than 1.0 A?

11. What is the resistance of a device that has a current of 3.4 A and a voltage of 40.0 V? (11.7) [T/I]

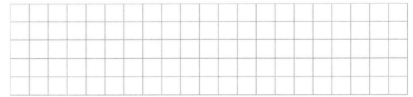

12. In **Figure 2**, the source voltage is 20.00 V, $R_1 = 12.25\ \Omega$, $R_2 = 6.00\ \Omega$, $R_3 = 10.00\ \Omega$. Use the circuit to solve the problems below. (11.8, 11.9) [T/I]

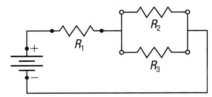

Figure 2

(a) Calculate the equivalent resistance of R_2 and R_3.

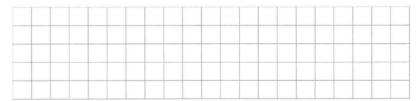

(b) Calculate the total resistance of the circuit.

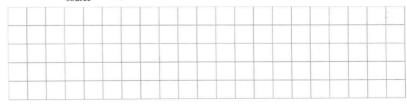

(c) Calculate I_{source} using Ohm's law.

Magnetic Fields

> **Vocabulary**
> magnetic field

Textbook pp. 548–552

MAIN IDEA: Magnetic fields are three-dimensional spaces that exert forces on metals and other materials that have magnetic properties.

1. Is the following statement true or false? If you think the statement is false, rewrite it to make it true: A magnetic field exists around a magnet even when the field itself is not exerting a force on any object. K/U

2. The pole of a permanent magnet that points toward Earth's north magnetic pole is labelled _____. K/U

3. Earth's south pole attracts the _____ pole of a permanent magnet, so the south pole itself must be a _____ magnetic pole. K/U

4. Earth's magnetic poles
   (a) change every thousand years
   (b) are permanent and never change
   (c) changed 780 000 years ago but will never change again
   (d) changed 780 000 years ago and may be slowly reversing K/U

5. For a single magnet, where are magnetic fields least intense? K/U

MAIN IDEA: Magnetic fields are strongest near the poles of magnets, never cross, and run north to south.

6. Is the following statement true or false? If you think the statement is false, rewrite it to make it true: Magnetic field lines always point north to south. C

> **LEARNING TIP**
>
> **Drawing Magnetic Field Lines**
> When drawing magnetic field lines outside of a magnet, always point arrows from north to south.

7. Draw the magnetic field lines for the bar magnet shown in **Figure 1**. C

Figure 1

8. Which statement about magnetic field lines is *not* true? K/U
   (a) Field lines cross paths near the poles of a magnet.
   (b) Field lines are closer together where the field is strongest.
   (c) Field lines are three-dimensional.
   (d) Field lines outside of a magnet run from north to south.

9. Draw field lines that include mini-compasses for the horseshoe magnet in **Figure 2**. C

Figure 2

10. Iron filings line up around two magnets, as shown in **Figure 3**. T/I C

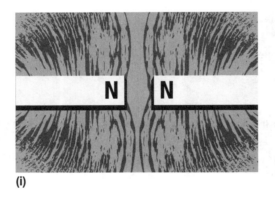

(i)

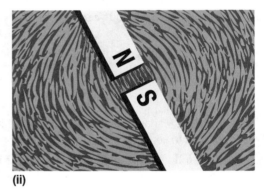

(ii)

Figure 3

(a) Label the direction of the magnetic field lines for each figure.

(b) Which figure shows attraction? How do you know?

(c) Which figure shows repulsion? How do you know?

(d) Identify where the magnetic field will be strongest in **Figure 3(ii)**.

(e) Explain how you know that the field is strongest at the place you identified in part (d). T/I C

11. Complete **Table 1**. K/U

Table 1 Magnets at Work

Magnet used in	Function
Maglev train	
particle accelerator	
MRI	
northern lights	
migrating animals	

Oersted's Discovery

> **Vocabulary**
>
> Oersted's principle   right-hand rule for a straight conductor

MAIN IDEA: Hans Christian Oersted's experiment proved that electricity and magnetism are linked and that a conductor with current running through it creates a magnetic field.

1. Oersted's experiment showed that when the direction of electric current is reversed, the magnetic field created by the current is _____. K/U

2. At any one point in a wire with current flowing through it, the magnetic force created by the current is _____ to the direction of the conventional current. K/U

3. What did Oersted's experiment prove? K/U

MAIN IDEA: The right-hand rule for a straight conductor states that when the thumb of your right hand points in the direction of the conventional current in a conductor, the curl of your fingers shows the direction of the magnetic field created around the conductor.

4. State two ways in which you can use the right-hand rule for a straight conductor. K/U C

> **LEARNING TIP**
>
> **Magnetic Field Direction**
> Regardless of whether you use the conventional current direction or the electron flow direction to determine which way current travels, the magnetic field around a current-carrying wire is the same.

5. Compare the right-hand rule and the left-hand rule for a straight conductor by completing **Table 1**. K/U

Table 1 Comparing the Right-Hand and Left-Hand Rules

Property	Right-hand rule	Left-hand rule
current		
direction of current		
thumb		
magnetic field		

6. **Figure 1** shows two wires with conventional current running through them. On each illustration, draw the direction of the compass needles to show the direction of the magnetic field. Draw the compass needles as arrowheads, with the tip of the arrow indicating north. [T/I] [C]

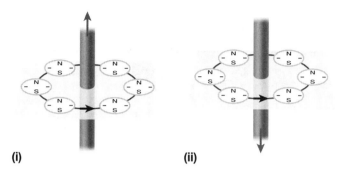

(i)   (ii)

Figure 1

MAIN IDEA: Oersted's discovery can be used to control the strength and direction of magnetic fields.

7. How can the following properties of magnetic fields be controlled? [K/U]

   (a) the strength of a magnetic field created by current flowing through a conductor

   (b) turning on and off the magnetic field created by current flowing through a conductor

   (c) the direction of the magnetic field created by current flowing through a conductor

8. Draw an X or a dot to show the direction of the current into the conductor in **Figure 2**. [K/U] [C]

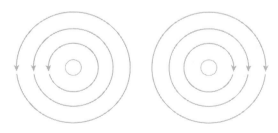

Figure 2

9. Label the following items on **Figure 3**. T/I C A

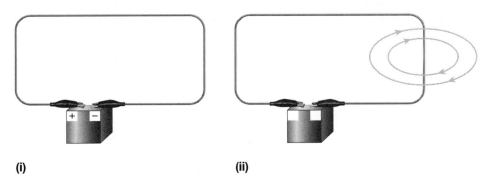

(i)   (ii)

Figure 3
(a) Show the magnetic field and its direction for Figure 3(i).
(b) Show the direction of conventional current for Figure 3(ii).
(c) In Figure 3(ii), show the direction of electron flow.
(d) In Figure 3(ii), indicate the poles of the power source.

10. Which of the diagrams in **Figure 4** is incorrect? Explain. T/I

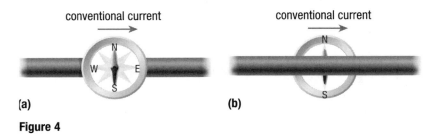

(a)   (b)

Figure 4

11. Magnets existed before Oersted made his discovery. Yet, the discovery has been described as something that changed the world significantly. What made Oersted's magnet different from the magnets that existed before his time? K/U C

12. A needle magnet hanging from a string near a conductor is shown in **Figure 5**. Which drawing shows what will happen when current flows through the conductor, (a) or (b)? Explain. K/U T/I

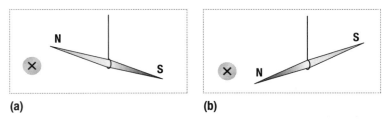

(a)   (b)

Figure 5

Wireless Electricity

Textbook pp. 557–558

MAIN IDEA: Transmission of electricity without wires is an idea that scientists are still pursuing today.

1. Why has the idea of transmitting electric power wirelessly attracted scientists? K/U

2. Why did the Tesla coil fail as a wireless provider of electricity? K/U

3. Which of the following statements most likely explains the need for very high voltages to produce arcing in the Tesla coil? K/U
   (a) Air has very low resistance, so current will not pass through air unless voltage is extremely high.
   (b) Very high voltages lower the resistance of air, allowing current to flow.
   (c) Air has very high resistance, so current will not pass through air unless voltage is extremely high.
   (d) All devices in Tesla's time required very large voltages to operate.

4. Compare different forms of portable electricity by completing **Table 1**. K/U

Table 1 Comparison of Forms of Portable Electricity

Form of portable electricity	Theoretical advantage	Actual drawbacks	Good option for the future?
Tesla coil			
wet and dry batteries			
NiMH batteries			
resonator			

5. (a) How will electricity be transmitted wirelessly using the technology developed at MIT?

   (b) What key insight will allow this technology to work over distances?

   (c) How will this technology avoid sending voltages to unintended targets such as people and walls? K/U

Solenoids

Vocabulary

solenoid   electromagnet   right-hand rule for a solenoid

MAIN IDEA: Magnetic fields created by current running through a wire interact in the same way that magnetic fields from permanent magnets interact.

1. Ampère took Oersted's experiment a step further by seeing how magnetic fields in two _____ wires interacted. K/U

2. Magnetic fields created by electric current in a loop
   (a) attract when the left side of the loop is positive
   (b) attract no matter which side of the loop is positive
   (c) repel when the right side of the loop is positive
   (d) repel no matter which side of the loop is positive K/U

3. Two parallel wires, wire 1 and wire 2, with electric current flowing through them are shown in **Figure 1**. K/U

> **LEARNING TIP**
>
> **Field Line Directions**
> When two field lines point in different directions, a repulsion force is applied. When field lines point in opposite directions, the forces attract.

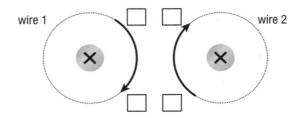

wire 1   wire 2

Figure 1

   (a) Label the north and south poles on the arrow for wire 1 and wire 2. Write your answers in the boxes provided.
   (b) What kind of force is created by the interaction of the two magnetic fields?

> **LEARNING TIP**
>
> **Right-Hand Rule for a Solenoid**
> A shorter way to state the right-hand rule for a solenoid is "fingers follow current, thumb points north."

4. Wire 3 and wire 4 in **Figure 2** are similar to the wires in Question 3 above, but wire 3 and wire 4 carry current in opposite directions. K/U

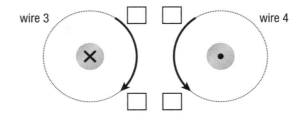

wire 3   wire 4

Figure 2

   (a) Label the north and south poles on the arrow for wire 3 and wire 4. Write your answers in the boxes provided.
   (b) What kind of force is created by the interaction of the two magnetic fields?

5. Review the diagrams you completed for Question 3 and Question 4. What can you conclude about magnetic fields in wires? K/U

MAIN IDEA: Running current through a coil creates a solenoid, which creates a magnetic field that is similar to that of a permanent bar magnet.

6. What is the most important way in which an electromagnet is different from a permanent magnet? K/U
    (a) Electromagnets are always more powerful than permanent magnets.
    (b) Electromagnets do not last as long as permanent magnets.
    (c) Electromagnets can be switched on and off easily.
    (d) Electromagnets are not as powerful as permanent magnets.

7. How can you increase the power of an electromagnet? K/U

8. (a) A single wire loop is shown in **Figure 3**. Draw the field lines.

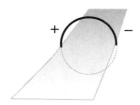

Figure 3

    (b) Now the single loop is connected with other loops to form a coil, as shown in **Figure 4**. Draw the field lines.

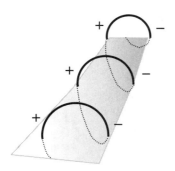

Figure 4

(c) Replace the separate field lines you drew in part (a) with combined field lines that show the magnetic field of the entire coil. Draw your answer onto **Figure 5**. How does this pattern compare to the magnetic field patterns for a permanent bar magnet? K/U C

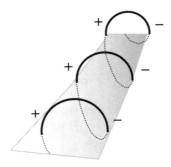

Figure 5

MAIN IDEA: The right-hand rule for a solenoid states that if the curled fingers of your hand match the direction of conventional current in the coil, then the direction of your thumb points to the north magnetic pole of the solenoid.

9. For **Figure 6**, use the right-hand rule for a solenoid to
   (a) identify the magnetic north pole of the coil

   (b) draw the magnetic field lines for the solenoid K/U C

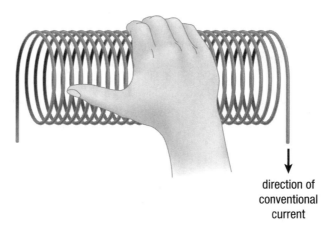

direction of
conventional
current

Figure 6

10. How did the invention of electromagnets and solenoids allow for the development of devices such as subwoofers, electric bells, and car-locking and car-unlocking mechanisms? K/U

The Motor Principle

Vocabulary

motor principle   right-hand rule for the motor principle

MAIN IDEA: Applying a magnetic field to a conductor that carries a current will cause the conductor to move.

1. Michael Faraday observed that electric current in a wire could create a magnetic field and cause a magnet to move. He then reasoned that one of the following might also be true:
   (a) An electric current could create current within a magnet.
   (b) A magnetic field could cause a current-carrying conductor to move.
   (c) A magnetic field could cause a non-current-carrying conductor to move.
   (d) A magnetic field could cause another magnet to move. K/U

2. Faraday used a bar magnet in a pool of mercury to cause a suspended wire to move, thus creating the world's first _____. K/U

3. Complete the flow chart to correctly describe the sequence of events in Faraday's Experiment. K/U C

   • The wire moves as a result of interaction between its magnetic field and the magnetic field of the bar magnet.
   • The knife switch is closed.
   • Current flows through the wire to the mercury to complete the circuit.
   • Current runs up the metal tower to the suspended wire.
   • The magnetic field from the bar magnet interacts with the magnetic field created by the current in the wire.

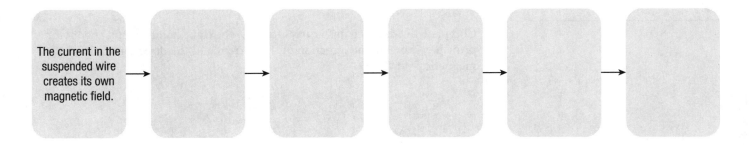

The current in the suspended wire creates its own magnetic field. →

4. When two magnetic field lines point in the same direction, a(n) _____ force results. When two magnetic field lines point in opposite directions, a(n) _____ force results. K/U

5. A diagram of Faraday's motor is shown in **Figure 2**. K/U T/I C

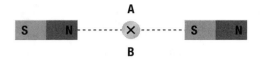

Figure 2

(a) Draw and label the magnetic fields that result from both the permanent magnets and the wire.

(b) At point A, are the magnetic fields pointing in the same direction or in different directions? What force on the wire will result?

(c) At point B, are the magnetic fields pointing in the same direction or in different directions? What force on the wire will result?

(d) In which direction will the wire be forced to move? Draw the force and final position of the wire after it moves.

LEARNING TIP

Right-Hand Rules
Note key differences between the right-hand rules for motors and coils. The fingers in the rule for coils point in the direction of the current. For motors, the fingers point in the direction of the external field.

MAIN IDEA: The motor principle states that when a conductor carries current in the presence of an external magnet, it experiences a force that is perpendicular to both the electric current and the magnetic field created by the electric current.

6. State the right-hand rule for the motor principle in your own words. K/U C

LEARNING TIP

Right-Hand Rule for the Motor Principle
A shorter way to state the right-hand rule for the motor principle is "thumb points in direction of current, fingers point south, palm faces force."

7. Complete the drawing in **Figure 3** to show the right-hand rule for the motor principle, showing the direction of the current and the direction of the magnetic field. K/U C

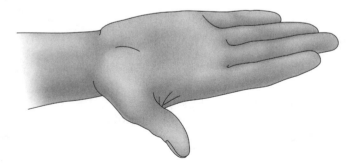

Figure 3

8. Complete **Table 1**. K/U

Table 1 Comparison of Electrical Meters

	Galvanometer	Ammeter	Voltmeter
Structure of device			
Measured quantity			
Connection to device being measured: series or parallel?			
Most of current flows through			

9. A galvanometer is shown in **Figure 4** below. Current flows in the direction shown. K/U C

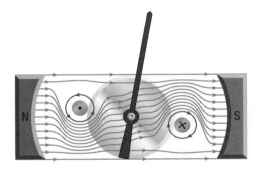

Figure 4

(a) Use the right-hand rule for the motor principle to determine the direction of the force for the wire on the left. Draw an arrow to represent the force.

(b) Determine the direction of the force for the wire on the right. Draw an arrow to represent the force.

(c) How will the two forces interact to move the meter?

(d) How does the device actually measure current? Explain.

The Direct Current Motor

MAIN IDEA: An electric DC motor uses electric current to produce continuous motion.

Textbook pp. 567–571

1. The key difference between a solenoid and a direct current motor is that the solenoid produces a(n) _____ motion, while the DC motor produces a(n) _____ motion. K/U

2. The moving part of a DC motor is the _____, and the stationary part of the motor is the _____. K/U

3. What three things does a split ring commutator do in a DC motor? K/U

4. Is the following statement true or false? If you think the statement is false, rewrite it to make it true: An electric current generates a magnetic field in a DC motor that interacts with an external stationary magnetic field to produce motion. K/U

STUDY TIP

Solving Motor Problems
When solving problems with motors, keep the right-hand rule for the motor principle in mind: point your fingers in the direction of the external magnetic field, and your thumb in the direction of the current. Your palm points to the force exerted.

MAIN IDEA: A split ring commutator interrupts the circuit and reverses the direction of the current and the magnetic field in the rotating part of the motor.

5. **Figure 1** shows step 1 of the turning of a DC motor. Notice that the split ring commutator is shown in two different coloured halves: the dark half and the light half. K/U

Step 1.

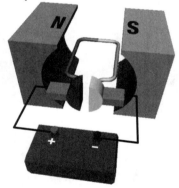

Figure 1

(a) In which half of the split ring commutator is the conventional current entering the circuit?

(b) In which half of the loop is the current entering? Draw an arrow on **Figure 1** to show the direction of the current.

(c) Using the right-hand rule for the motor principle, in which direction is the force on the left edge of the loop being exerted? What kind of rotation will this begin? Draw an arrow to show the direction of the force on the loop.

6. **Figure 2** shows step 2 of the DC motor cycle. K/U

Step 2.

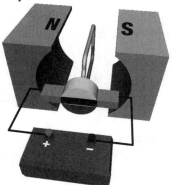

Figure 2

(a) In which half of the split ring commutator is the conventional current entering the circuit?

(b) In which half of the loop is the current entering?

(c) What motion will occur during this step? Explain.

7. **Figure 3** shows step 3 of the DC motor cycle.

Step 3.

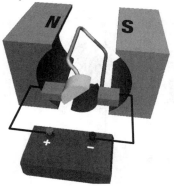

Figure 3

(a) In which half of the split ring commutator does the conventional current enter the circuit?

(b) In which half of the loop is the current entering? Draw an arrow to show the direction of the current.

(c) Compare the current in step 3 and step 1. Are the two currents travelling in the same direction or in opposite directions? Explain.

(d) From step 1 to step 3, how would you describe the change in the direction of the current? What caused this change?

(e) From step 1 to step 3, how would you describe the change in the direction of the loop? What caused this change?

8. To increase the efficiency of DC motors, designers use a split ring commutator that has _____. **K/U**

9. Steps for an armature DC motor are shown in **Figure 4**, **Figure 5**, and **Figure 6**. Complete **Table 1**, **Table 2**, and **Table 3** for each step. **T/I**

Table 1 Step 1

Current directed at split ring:	
Thumb points:	
North side of coil located on which side?	
Interaction:	
Movement:	

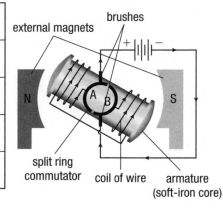

Figure 4

Table 2 Step 2

Current directed at split ring:	
Thumb points:	
North side of coil located on which side?	
Interaction:	
Movement:	

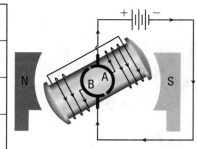

Figure 5

Table 3 Step 3

Current directed at split ring:	
Thumb points:	
North side of coil located on which side?	
Interaction:	
Movement:	

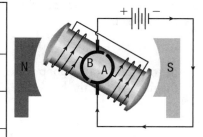

Figure 6

Magnetic Resonance Imaging

Textbook pp. 572–573

MAIN IDEA: Magnetic resonance imaging provides a unique three-dimensional view of the interior of the human body.

1. Is the following statement true or false? If you think the statement is false, rewrite it to make it true: The key advantage that magnetic resonance imaging (MRI) has over X-ray and ultrasound technology is that it can provide detailed images of soft tissues. [K/U]

2. List four disadvantages of MRI technology. [K/U]

3. What might prevent someone with metal implants in their body from using an MRI machine? [K/U]

4. Which of the following identifies the most common reason that people go to private clinics and pay for an MRI scan out of their own pockets? [K/U]
   (a) They do not want to wait for a long period of time to get their results.
   (b) They do not trust medical treatments administered by government agencies.
   (c) They are usually from the United States and do not have medical insurance.
   (d) They need special types of MRI procedures because they have pacemakers or implants.

5. **Table 1** lists some reasons for and against taking an MRI treatment. Complete the table. [K/U] [C]

Table 1 Pros and Cons of MRI Treatment

Reason for MRI	Reason against MRI
MRI will give the best image of the problem.	
	Private MRI facilities are expensive.
MRI when covered by provincial health care is free of charge.	
There are many MRI machines in Canada.	
	Patients with claustrophobia may not be able to undergo MRI.
Most people can undergo MRI treatments without any problem.	

Electromagnetism

Complete the graphic organizer below to review what you have learned about electromagnetism. To help you study the concepts in this chapter, add to this organizer your own ideas, examples, and diagrams. You could also create your own graphic organizer.

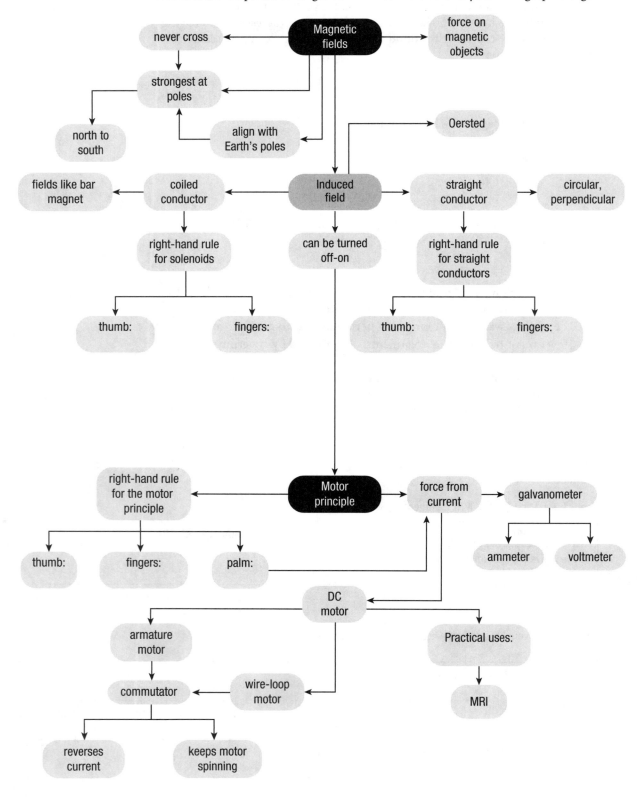

1. Which drawing in **Figure 1** accurately labels Earth's magnetic poles? (12.1) K/U

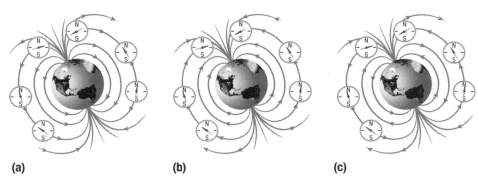

	K/U	Knowledge/Understanding
	T/I	Thinking/Investigation
	C	Communication
	A	Application

(a)   (b)   (c)

Figure 1

2. What did Oersted's experiment prove? (12.2) K/U
   (a) Magnetic fields create electric currents.
   (b) An electric current in a conductor creates a magnetic field that is perpendicular to the current.
   (c) An electric current in a conductor creates a magnetic field that is parallel to the current.
   (d) All conductors have circular-shaped magnetic fields surrounding them.

3. Identify three ways to change the magnetic field that is created by current running through a straight conductor. (12.2) K/U

4. What drawback do even the best rechargeable batteries have? (12.3) K/U

5. (a) Draw a cross-sectional dot or X diagram on **Figure 2** to show the direction of current and the direction of the magnetic field at positions A and B on the wire.

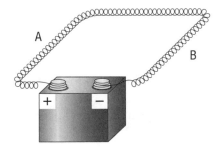

Figure 2

   (b) In which direction is the current flowing at point A? at point B?

(c) What would happen if you brought these two sides of the wire close together? (12.2) K/U

6. Draw the direction of the north and south poles and the field lines for the solenoid in **Figure 3**. (12.4) T/I

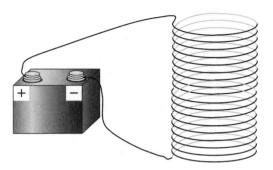

Figure 3

7. Use the right-hand rule for the motor principle to determine the direction of force on the wire in **Figure 4**. On **Figure 4**, draw the magnetic field lines, and draw the force as a block arrow. (12.5) T/I

Figure 4

8. (a) On which side of the loop is conventional current entering the DC motor in **Figure 5**?

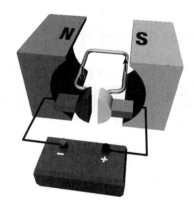

Figure 5

(b) In which direction will the loop turn? Explain how you know. (12.6) T/I

9. What danger do MRI examinations pose? (12.7) K/U

Electromagnetic Induction

Vocabulary		Textbook pp. 588–591
electromagnetic induction	law of electromagnetic induction	

MAIN IDEA: A change in a magnetic field will cause a current to flow in a nearby conductor.

1. The law of electromagnetic induction states that any change in a
_____ near a conductor creates a voltage in the conductor
and an induced _____. K/U

2. Is the following statement true or false? If you think the statement is false, rewrite it to make it true: Since a constant current produces a constant magnetic field, a constant magnetic field will induce a constant current. K/U

> **LEARNING TIP**
>
> **Currents**
> All currents create a magnetic field, so one current can indirectly induce a second current.

MAIN IDEA: Faraday's ring experiment helped him formulate the law of electromagnetic induction.

3. In his Faraday ring experiment, Michael Faraday found which of the following to be true? K/U
   (a) Current was created in the conducting wire as long as the magnet was moving.
   (b) Current was created in the conducting wire only when the magnet was not touching the wire.
   (c) Current was created in the conducting wire only when a permanent magnet was used.
   (d) Current was created in the conducting wire only when an electromagnet was used.

4. Use what you have learned about the relationship between electric current and magnetic fields to complete **Table 1**. K/U

Table 1 Currents, Fields, and Induced Currents

Current	Field		Induced current	
Type	Field produced	Field direction	Field induces current?	Duration of induced current
steady				
changing				

5. Why was Faraday's discovery of electromagnetic induction particularly significant? K/U

   (a) Before Faraday's discovery, scientists had no way of supplying current to an electrical device.

   (b) Before Faraday's discovery, scientists were able to generate electricity only in small quantities.

   (c) Before Faraday's discovery, scientists had no practical uses for electric devices.

   (d) Before Faraday's discovery, scientists could generate electricity using batteries or electric cells only.

6. Is the following statement true or false? If you think the statement is false, rewrite it to make it true: Current induced by an electromagnet is greater than current induced by a permanent magnet. K/U

MAIN IDEA: There are different ways that you can change the amount of current in a conductor.

7. **Table 2** lists the factors that increase the amount of current generated using electromagnetic induction. For each factor, write the reason for the increase. K/U

Table 2 Factors that Increase Induced Current

Factor	Reason for increase
coiled conductor	
more loops in coil	
magnetic field rate of change	
strength of magnetic field	

8. A classmate is trying to repeat Faraday's induction experiment using a Faraday ring. When you walk into the classroom, you see the setup shown in **Figure 1**. The galvanometer reads zero. You test the power supply and discover there is power. Why is there no current? What can you do to induce current? T/I

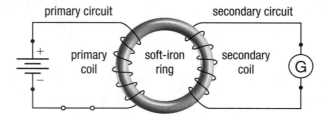

primary circuit   secondary circuit

primary coil   soft-iron ring   secondary coil   G

Figure 1

Lenz's Law

Textbook pp. 592–594

> **Vocabulary**
> Lenz's law

MAIN IDEA: Lenz's law relates the direction of an induced current to the direction of the magnetic field that created it.

1. Lenz's law states that the electric current induced by a changing magnetic field will flow in the direction that _____ the change that induced the current. K/U

2. Is the following statement true or false? If you think the statement is false, rewrite it to make it true: When applying Lenz's law, use the right-hand rule for straight conductors. K/U

3. **Figure 1** shows a bar magnet being pushed into a coil. K/U

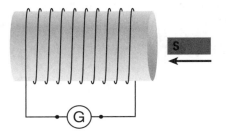

Figure 1

> **STUDY TIP**
>
> **Remembering Lenz's Law**
> The coil opposes whatever the magnet is trying to do. If north is moving in, the coil repels it with a north. If north is moving out, the coil attracts it with a south.

(a) What force do you feel when you push the south pole of the magnet into a coil?

(b) Which pole is on the right side of the solenoid?

(c) How do you know that your answer to (b) is correct?

(d) Determine the direction of the current in the coil. Draw an arrow to show the current on the diagram.

4. **Figure 2** shows a bar magnet exiting a coil. K/U

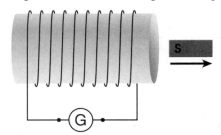

Figure 2

(a) What force do you feel when you pull the south pole of the magnet out of the coil?

(b) Which pole is on the right side of the solenoid?

(c) In which direction is the conventional current in the coil travelling? Draw the current.

(d) If you moved the magnet in and out repeatedly, what current pattern will be reflected in the galvanometer?

(e) List two ways that you can increase the magnitude of the current. K/U

5. A bar magnet is pushed into a solenoid. T/I C
   (a) What evidence do you see that energy is transformed from one form to another?

   (b) What evidence do you see that energy is conserved?

6. Arrange the steps below in the order that correctly describes the sequence of events for the application of brakes in a drop tower ride. K/U
   ___(a) An electric current is induced in the copper by the moving magnetic field.
   ___(b) The cart on the ride free falls for about 45 m.
   ___(c) The induced current produces its own magnetic field.
   ___(d) The two opposing forces slow the cart to a halt.
   ___(e) Permanent magnets on the bottom of each cart slide past copper conductor strips.
   ___(f) The magnetic field created by the induced current opposes the field that created it.

Alternating Current

Vocabulary

alternating current

Textbook pp. 595–598

MAIN IDEA: Alternating current is electric current that periodically reverses direction.

1. If you push a permanent magnet in and out of a coil, a(n)
   _____ electric current will be produced. K/U

2. Is the following statement true or false? If you think the statement is false,
   rewrite it to make it true: The fact that current switches direction in alternating
   current means that voltage also alternates in charge. K/U

3. Why did alternating current ultimately prevail over direct current for general
   household use? K/U

4. In a hair dryer that uses alternating current, the same electrons are moving
   back and forth without actually flowing around a circuit. Nevertheless, the
   fact that the hair dryer blows hot air provides proof that the moving electrons
   transfer _____ to the device. A

5. One of the following systems cannot be used to generate alternating current.
   Identify the system. K/U
   (a) a system whose current is produced by a back-and-forth motion of a
       permanent magnet
   (b) a system whose current is produced by a steady magnetic field
   (c) a system whose current is produced by a back-and-forth motion of an
       electromagnet
   (d) a system whose current is produced by an electromagnet with voltage that
       changes regularly

6. Is the following statement true or false? If you think the statement is false, rewrite
   it to make it true: A current of 60 Hz has a value of 60 volts per second. K/U

7. How many times per second does a 60 Hz current drop to a value of zero? K/U
   (a) 0
   (b) 60
   (c) 120
   (d) 240

8. Compare direct current and alternating current by completing **Table 1**. K/U

Table 1 Direct and Alternating Current

	Direct current	**Alternating current**
typically produced by		
one-way or two-way current		
frequency of voltage change		
original promoter		
advantage		
follows Ohm's law, $V = IR$ (yes or no)		

MAIN IDEA: Home electrical systems are typically 120 V or 240 V and are protected by fuses, circuit breakers, and other safety devices.

9. How does the actual maximum voltage in a typical home compare to the typical effective voltage of 240 V that homes receive? K/U
   (a) The maximum voltage is equal to the effective voltage.
   (b) The maximum voltage is greater than the effective voltage.
   (c) The maximum voltage is less than the effective voltage.
   (d) The maximum voltage is twice the effective voltage.

10. An electrician measures the voltage between two wires in the distribution panel of a house and determines the potential difference to be 120 V. K/U
   (a) What colours might these two wires have?

   (b) What colours will these two wires *not* have?

11. **Figure 1** shows a simplified circuit for a house. A power bar for one outlet has three appliances, A, B, and C, that all use a lot of current. K/U T/I

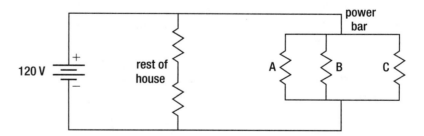

Figure 1

   (a) What is the voltage for the entire house? for the single outlet? for appliances A, B, and C?

   (b) Why might this outlet cause a fuse or circuit breaker to blow?

Electricity Generation

Vocabulary

electric generator

Textbook pp. 599–604

MAIN IDEA: A single-loop alternating current generator uses an external force to spin a wire loop inside a magnetic field to generate alternating current.

1. An AC generator needs a(n) _____ source of energy to generate electric current. K/U

2. Is the following statement true or false? If you think the statement is false, rewrite it to make it true: Any source of energy that can turn a loop inside a magnetic field in an AC generator can be used to generate electric current. K/U

3. In a single-loop AC generator, _____ are used to change the direction of the current that is generated. K/U

4. Lenz's law requires that
   (a) the loop in an AC generator must turn clockwise
   (b) the loop in an AC generator must turn counterclockwise
   (c) work must be done to turn the loop in an AC generator
   (d) the loop in a single-loop AC generator switches directions as it turns K/U

5. List two different ways to increase the current generated by a single-loop AC generator. K/U

LEARNING TIP

Magnetic Field Lines
Adjacent magnetic field lines that run in the same direction indicate repulsion. Lines that run in opposite directions indicate attraction.

6. **Figure 1** shows a single-loop AC generator. The external force on the generator is moving the loop in a counterclockwise direction. K/U T/I

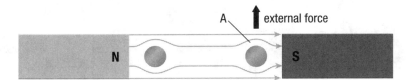

external force

Figure 1

   (a) To satisfy Lenz's law, what type of force must exist at point A, close to the magnet's south pole: an attraction or a repulsion?

   (b) Draw the direction of the force at point A.

   (c) Mark the direction of the current in the wire below point A.

7. **Figure 2** shows a single-loop AC generator. K/U

Figure 2

(a) Draw arrows to indicate the direction of the conventional current in the figure.

(b) Into which slip ring is the current headed?

(c) Draw arrows to show the current entering the galvanometer. Which side of the galvanometer does the conventional current enter?

(d) Does the galvanometer show a positive or a negative reading? Draw the meter needle in the diagram.

8. **Figure 3** shows the position of a loop AC generator as the loop spins clockwise. Show the position of each reading on the graph in **Figure 4** below. Label the positions (a), (b), (c), and (d) on the graph to correspond to each diagram. T/I

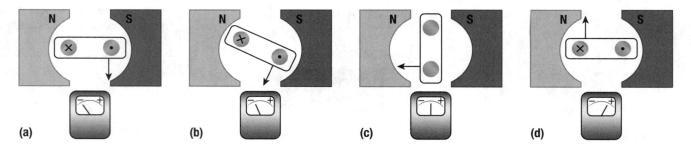

(a)   (b)   (c)   (d)

Figure 3

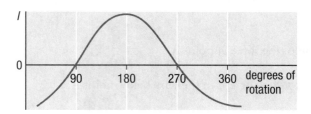

Figure 4

9. (a) Why does a DC generator have a split ring commutator rather than slip rings? What is the purpose of the split ring commutator?

   (b) AC generators are very common and efficient in generating usable current. What purpose does a DC generator serve? K/U

MAIN IDEA: Spinning an armature rather than a coil provides a more efficient way of generating AC current.

10. **Figure 5** shows a coil-type AC generator being rotated by an external force in a counterclockwise direction. K/U T/I

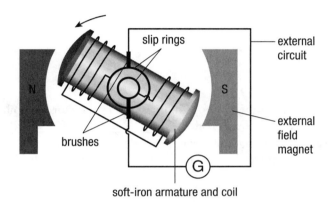

Figure 5

   (a) Which pole is the left (shaded) part of the armature? Explain how you know.

   (b) Which rule can you use to find the direction of the current in the diagram?

   (c) Draw arrows to show the current on the diagram.

Transformers

Textbook pp. 605–609

Vocabulary

transformer   step-down transformer   step-up transformer

MAIN IDEA: A transformer can change the amount of voltage or current that a power source provides.

1. An electric device requires 8 V to operate. In a typical house, the device must use a(n) _____ transformer to _____ the home voltage to 8 V. K/U

2. A transformer uses _____ current in the primary coil to induce _____ current in the secondary coil. K/U
   (a) direct; direct
   (b) alternating; direct
   (c) direct; alternating
   (d) alternating; alternating

3. (a) When you increase the number of loops in the primary transformer coil, the strength of the magnetic field created _____.
   (b) How does increasing the strength of a magnetic field in a transformer's primary coil change the current and voltage that are induced by the field?

   (c) How does increasing the number of loops in the secondary coil of a transformer change the voltage in the secondary coil? K/U

4. **Figure 1** shows two transformers. K/U

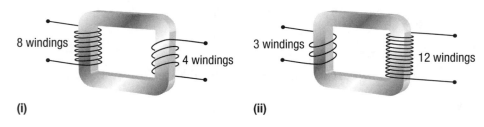

(i)   (ii)

Figure 1

(a) What kind of transformer is transformer (i)? Explain your answer.

(b) What kind of transformer is transformer (ii)? Explain your answer.

(c) The input voltage of 20 V is provided for transformer (ii). Will the output voltage be greater or less than 20 V?

(d) A transformer is needed to take a 240 V home line down to 120 V. Which transformer would be appropriate for this task? Explain your answer.

(e) The primary coil of transformer (i) receives a 20 V input from a DC power supply. How many volts will the secondary coil provide as output?

5. (a) Power going into the primary coil of a transformer, P_p, must be equal to the power coming out of the secondary coil, P_s, and power equals the product of voltage and current, $P = VI$. Show algebraically that voltage and current are inversely proportional.

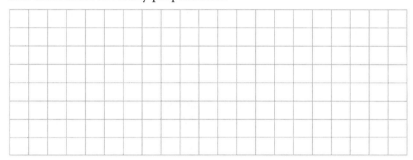

(b) Given that voltage is directly proportional to the number of windings in a coil, show that current, I, is inversely proportional to N, the number of windings in a coil. T/I

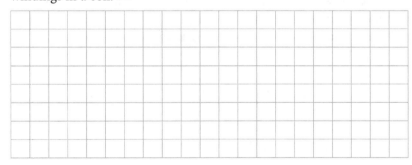

6. A step-up transformer has 40 windings in the primary coil and 200 windings in the secondary coil. The input voltage into the primary coil is 8.6 V. Calculate the output voltage. T/I

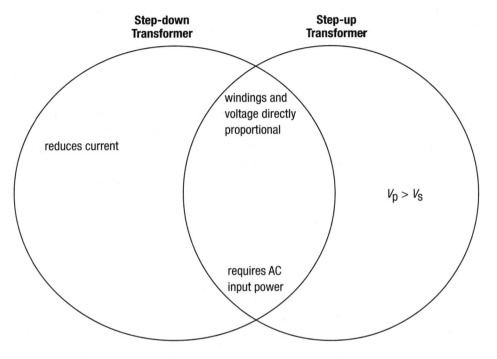

STUDY TIP

Venn Diagrams

When filling in a Venn diagram, it is often helpful to begin with the items that uniquely identify each category. Then move on to the items shared.

7. Complete the Venn diagram for a step-up transformer and a step-down transformer. Use the terms supplied. K/U C

- increases current
- windings: more primary than secondary
- windings: more secondary than primary
- voltage and current inversely proportional
- windings and current inversely proportional

- $V_p < V_s$
- $I_s > I_p$
- $I_s < I_p$
- $\Delta E_p = \Delta E_s$

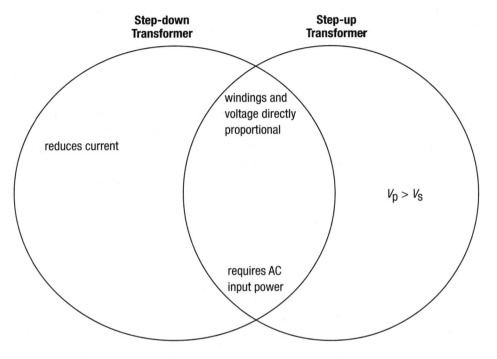

Step-down Transformer   **Step-up Transformer**

reduces current

windings and voltage directly proportional

requires AC input power

$V_p > V_s$

LEARNING TIP

Transformer Equations

You can remember one equation:

$$\frac{V_p}{V_s} = \frac{I_s}{I_p} = \frac{N_p}{N_s}$$

8. A step-down transformer in a device takes an input voltage of 120.00 V and reduces it to 8.00 V. The primary coil has 180 windings, and the current in the secondary coil is 0.40 A. T/I

(a) Calculate the number of windings in the secondary coil.

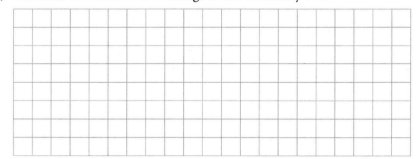

(b) Calculate the current in the primary coil.

Power Plants and the Electrical Grid

MAIN IDEA: A power plant needs to use transformers and AC power to maximize efficiency.

Textbook pp. 610–612

1. Modern power plants generate _____ current because it results in much less waste as thermal energy than _____ current. K/U

2. Is the following statement true or false? If you think the statement is false, rewrite it to make it true: Lowering the resistance of power lines would result in less energy wasted as thermal energy. K/U

3. In modern power plants, power is transmitted at _____ voltages and _____ currents to reduce the loss of thermal energy. K/U

4. **Table 1** compares DC power and AC power in power plants. Use "yes" or "no" responses to complete the table. K/U

Table 1 Comparing AC and DC Power

Property	DC power	AC power
provides enough initial voltage and current		
generates unusable thermal energy as waste		
voltage and current can be changed by transformer		
thermal energy loss can be minimized with low currents		

5. Which of the following best explains why AC power is more efficient than DC power? K/U
   (a) Less energy is lost from AC power in a power line than DC power.
   (b) A transformer can be used with AC power, but not DC power, to step voltage up and down and transmit low-current/high-voltage power.
   (c) DC power cannot provide enough current for usage by power plant customers, and DC voltage fluctuates and is unreliable over time.
   (d) DC power provides voltages that are too dangerous for usage by power plant customers.

6. Why do power plants frequently need to sell some of the power they generate? K/U

7. A wind turbine produces 150.0 kW of power at 500 V with a current of 0.5 kA. T/I
   (a) With a power line resistance of 0.1 Ω, calculate the amount of power that is wasted as thermal energy in this system.

LEARNING TIP

Voltage and Current
In trying to understand the strategy that power plants employ, keep in mind that since $V = IR$, raising the voltage of a plant's output allows a much smaller current to supply the same amount of power. Smaller current means much less waste, which makes power plants much more efficient.

(b) What percent of energy is wasted in this system?

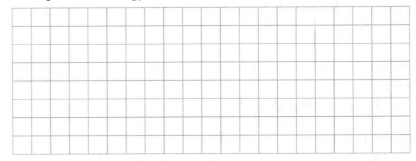

(c) Suppose the current is lowered to 0.1 kA. Predict whether efficiency will increase or decrease. Explain your prediction.

(d) Test your prediction from (c) algebraically. T/I

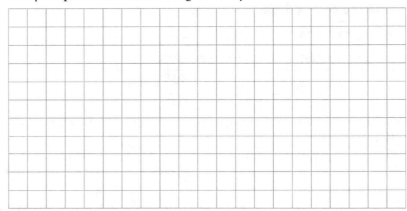

8. The towers that carry long-distance transmission lines are much taller than telephone poles. Explain why. K/U C

9. On a hot summer day, demand for power increases at a hydroelectric power plant. List two ways in which the plant can keep up with demand. K/U C

Electromagnetic Induction

Use the graphic organizer below to study the concepts you learned in Chapter 13.
You can add to this organizer or create your own for additional review.

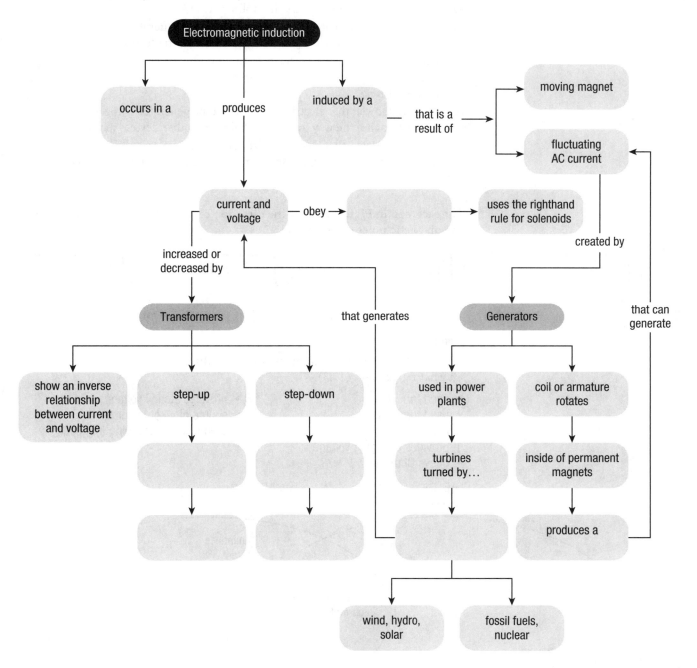

K/U Knowledge/Understanding
T/I Thinking/Investigation
C Communication
A Application

1. In a Faraday ring, current will flow in the secondary coil as long as current in the primary coil continues to _____. (13.1) K/U

2. How did Faraday's discovery of electromagnetic induction pave the way to exciting discoveries in the years that followed? (13.1) K/U
   (a) Faraday showed that electric current could be generated on demand, paving the way for battery-operated devices in the future.
   (b) Faraday showed that electric current could be generated using changing magnetic fields, paving the way for electric lights and other devices in the future.
   (c) Faraday showed that electric current could be generated using a steady direct current, paving the way for electric lights and other devices in the future.
   (d) Faraday showed that electric current could be generated using very strong magnetic fields, paving the way for electric lights and other devices in the future.

3. For each coil in **Figure 1**, draw the direction of the induced current and label the magnetic poles of the coil. (13.2) T/I

(a)

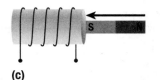
(b)

(c)

(d)

Figure 1

4. Use the phrases below to complete the Venn diagram for direct current and alternating current. (13.3) K/U

- used for: TV
- used for: laptop
- creates a magnetic field
- provides changing voltage
- obeys Ohm's law, $V = IR$

- provides steady voltage
- source of electric current
- produced by: changing magnetic field

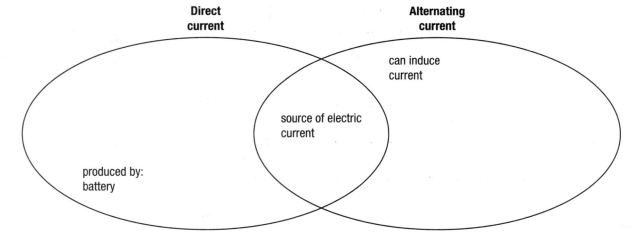

Direct current

Alternating current

can induce current

source of electric current

produced by: battery

5. **Figure 2** shows two AC generators. Determine the poles of the armature and the direction of rotation for (a) and (b). Draw your answers on the diagram. (13.4) K/U

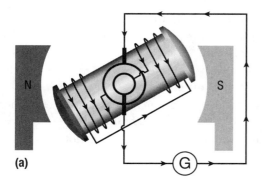 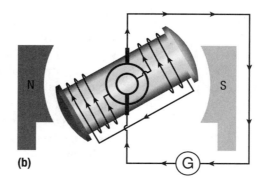

(a) **(b)**

Figure 2

6. A step-up transformer with 100 windings in the secondary coil takes an input voltage of 24.0 V and produces an output voltage of 120.0 V. The current in the primary coil is 0.25 A. (13.5) K/U T/I

   (a) Calculate the number of windings in the primary coil.

   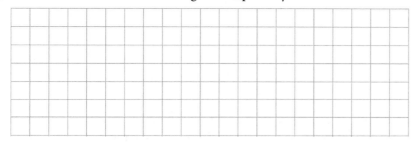

   (b) Calculate the current in the secondary coil.

   (c) Identify the voltage and current changes that the transformer caused. Which quantity increased? Which quantity decreased? How do you explain these changes?

7. A generator produces 40.0 MW of power with an initial current of 4.0 kA. A transformer is used to decrease the current to 0.40 kA. Will the voltage coming out of the transformer increase or decrease? Explain your answer. (13.6) T/I

K/U   Knowledge/Understanding
T/I   Thinking/Investigation
C   Communication
A   Application

1. Which of the following statements is true? (11.6) K/U
   (a) Inserting a resistor in a series circuit increases the total resistance of the circuit and the current in the circuit.
   (b) Inserting a resistor in a series circuit decreases the total resistance of the circuit and increases the current in the circuit.
   (c) Inserting resistor in parallel with a circuit increases the total resistance of the circuit and decreases the current in the circuit.
   (d) Inserting a resistor in parallel with a circuit decreases the total resistance of the circuit and increases the current in the circuit.

2. Forcing electrons to be closer together increases their _____. (11.1) K/U

3. Calculate the electric potential difference that will result when 2250 J of potential energy is transformed to move 27.5 C of electrons. (11.3) T/I

4. A mini-TV requires 4.2 C of electrons to be fully charged. The charger for the device charges at a rate of 0.6 mA. How long does it take to fully charge the device? (11.5) T/I

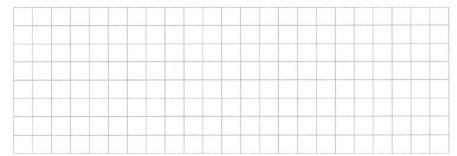

5. In **Figure 1**, the source voltage is 32 V, R_1 = 10.0 Ω, R_2 = 4.0 Ω, R_3 = 8.0 Ω, and R_4 = 7.33 Ω. Calculate I_{source} using Ohm's law. (11.7, 11.8, 11.9) T/I

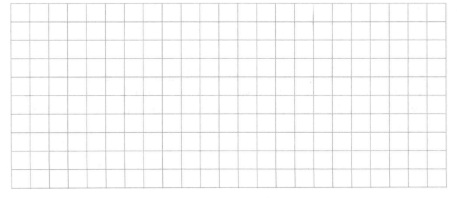

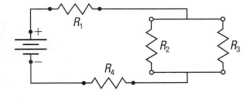

Figure 1

6. The magnetic field created by a solenoid is shown in **Figure 2**. Draw the wires to hook up the power source to the solenoid. Label the poles for the power supply and the solenoid. (12.4) 🔲

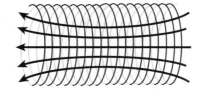

Figure 2

7. **Figure 3** shows an armature DC motor. Label the poles of the power source, and add arrows to show the direction in which this armature DC motor will spin. (12.6) 🔲

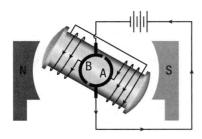

Figure 3

8. A transformer with 200 windings in the primary coil and a primary current of 0.75 A takes an input voltage of 80.0 V and produces an output voltage of 140 V. Calculate the number of windings in the secondary coil, and calculate the amount of current that runs through the secondary coil. (13.5) 🔲

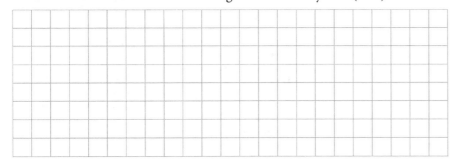

9. A generator produces 80.0 MW of power with an initial current of 5.0 kA. A transformer is used to decrease the current to 0.80 kA. How much more efficient will the generator become as a result of this reduction in current if resistance is 0.20 Ω? (13.6) 🔲

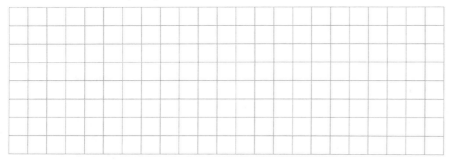

Answers

These pages include numerical and short answers to chapter section questions, Chapter Questions, and Unit Questions.

Unit 1

1.1, pp. 2–3
2. (a) 2100 m
   (b) 630 m [N]
5. 280 m [E]

1.2, pp. 4–6
1. 250 m
2. (a) 30.7 m/s
   (b) 27.9 m/s
3. 24 min
4. 3.6 m/s [E]
5. (a) 0.15 m/s [W]
   (b) 0.27 m/s

1.3, pp. 7–10
1. 3800 m/s^2
2. (a) 28.6 m/s [S]
   (b) 14.5 m/s [N]
3. (a) 2.0×10^2 m [E]
   (b) 140 m [E]
   (c) at $t = 4.0$ s,
   $a = 6.3$ m/s^2 [E]
   at $t = 6.0$ s, $a = 0$ m/s^2
4. (a) at $t = 0$ s,
   $\vec{v}_{inst} = 40$ m/s [N]
   at $t = 5$ s,
   $\vec{v}_{inst} = 20$ m/s [N]
   at $t = 10$ s, $\vec{v}_{inst} = 0$ m/s
   (b) at $t = 12$ s, $\vec{v}_{inst} = 8$ m/s [S]
   at $t = 15$ s,
   $\vec{v}_{inst} = 2.0 \times 10$ m/s [S]
   at $t = 18$ s,
   $\vec{v}_{inst} = 32$ m/s [S]
(c) 4 m/s^2 [S]

1.4, pp. 11–12
1. (b)
3. (a) 3.0 s and 10 s
   (b) 16 m/s [W]
   (c) 15 m/s [E]

1.5, pp. 13–15
1. (a) 8.0 s
   (b) 80 m
2. 330 m/s
3. (a) in 2.0 s, car travels 6.2 m [E]
   in 2.0 s, truck travels
   3.0×10 m [E]
   in 8.0 s, car travels 99 m [E]
   in 8.0 s, truck travels
   120 m [E]
   (b) truck passes car at 0 s,
   car passes truck at 9.7 s
   (c) truck passes car at
   intersection,
   car passes truck 150 m [E]
   past intersection
4. (a) 1.859 s
   (b) 10.2 m/s [down]

1.6, pp. 16–18
1. (c)
2. (a) 2.0 s
   (b) at $t = 0.50$ s,
   $\vec{v} = 4.9$ m/s [down]
   at $t = 1.5$ s,
   $\vec{v} = 15$ m/s [down]
   at impact,
   $\vec{v} = 2.0 \times 10$ m/s [down]
3. (a) 5400 m
   (b) 66 s
   (c) 320 m/s [down]
   (d) no
4. (a) before bounce:
   $v = 6.3$ m/s [down];
   after bounce:
   $v = 5.6$ m/s [up]

Chapter 1 Questions, pp. 21–22
1. (c)
2. (a) F
   (b) T
3. (a) 15.0 m [N]
   (b) 15.0 m [N]
4. 2.0×10 m/s^2 [W]
5. (a) 3.0 m/s [E]
   (b) 4.0×10 m [E]
6. (a) 2.5 m
   (b) 0.71 s

2.1, pp. 23–25
1. (b)
5. 16 m [N 35° W]
6. (a) 78 mm [E 68° N]
   (b) 5.6 mm/s [E 68° N]

2.2, pp. 26–28
1. F
2. Pythagorean theorem,
   direction
3. $\Delta d_x = 26.24$ m [W]
   $\Delta d_y = 18.35$ m [S]
4. 16.1 m [E 45.9° N]
5. (a) 0.04 h
   (c) 300 m [E]
   (d) 25 km/h [N 53° E]

2.3, pp. 29–31
1. F
2. (c)
4. (b) 2.6 s
   (c) 55 m
   (d) 8.0 m
5. (a) 32 m
   (b) 19 m/s [right 56° down]

2.4, p. 32
1. constant, gravity
2. (b)

2.5, p. 33
1. T
2. (c)

Chapter 2 Questions, pp. 35–36
1. free fall, mass
2. (a) 39 m [E 66° N]
   (b) 0.50 m/s [E]
3. 17 m [E 28° N]
4. (b) 2.78 s
   (c) 105 m
   (d) 9.43 m

Unit 1 Questions, pp. 37–38
1. (b)
2. (c)
3. (a) F
   (b) F
7. (a) 7.5 min
   (b) 38 m [S]
   (c) 0.50 km/h [E 37° S]

Unit 2

3.1, pp. 40–42
2. newton, N
7. gravity
9. 4.9 N [down]
11. 2020 N [up]

3.2, pp. 43–45
1. change in motion
4. F
7. (a) no
   (b) yes
   (c) yes
   (d) yes
   (e) yes
   (f) no
8. (b) 2.0 N [opposing the
   applied force]
9. (b) 0 N
   (c) 46 N [backward]

3.3, pp. 46–49
1. smaller, larger; larger, smaller;
   smaller, larger
2. 0.25
3. 4
4. (a) the net force
   (c) 8.2 m/s^2 [right]
5. 1.4 kg
6. 22 m/s [down]
7. (a) 2.9 N [down]
   (b) 4.9 m/s^2 [down]
8. 24 N

3.4, pp. 50–51
3. no delay
5. (a) yes
   (b) yes
6. (a) both

3.5, pp. 52–53
3. 1500 N
4. (a) 1.8 kg
   (b) 5.9 N
   (c) 3.3 m/s^2
7. (a) 2.77 m/s^2 [forward]
   (b) 3490 N [forward]
   (c) 139 m [forward]

3.6, p. 54
1. (b)
3. (b)

Chapter 3 Questions, pp. 56–57
2. F
3. (b)
5. (b) $F_g = mg$
   (c) $F_g = mg$
6. 0 N
8. 4.1 N

4.1, pp. 58–60
2. (b) 0 m/s [down],
   9.8 m/s^2 [down]
   (c) 0 N
3. (a) increased
   (b) unchanged
   (c) increased
4. (b) air resistance, gravity
   (c) $\vec{F}_{air} = -\vec{F}_g$
9. 3.6 kg

4.2, pp. 61–62
2. (b)
3. increase
5. (d)
6. (a) sliding friction
   (b) rolling friction
   (c) fluid friction
9. (a) 8.8 N
   (b) 8.8 N
   (c) 1.3 N
   (d) 0.15
10. 1.6 N

4.3, pp. 63–65
1. 370 N
4. (a) 490 N
   (b) 4.1 m/s^2 [forward]
7. (b) 960 N

4.4, pp. 66–67
1. F
2. static
6. high, low

4.5, pp. 68–69
2. (a) leather/rubber
   (b) longer, faster
   (c) heavier
4. (c)

Chapter 4 Questions, pp. 72–73

1. (c)
5. increases
7. (a) kinetic
   (b) static
11. (a) 120 N
    (b) 98 N

Unit 2 Questions, pp. 74–75

1. (a)
3. (a) same magnitude
   (b) opposite directions
   (c) the hand throwing the ball
   (d) at the same time
   (d) no
4. (b) 1.0×10 N

Unit 3

5.1, pp. 77–79

1. $W = F\Delta d$
2. newton metre, joule
4. 138 J
6. 120 J
7. A and B
8. 3.6×10^2 J
9. positive

5.2, pp. 80–81

1. kinetic, potential
2. 25 J
5. 620 J
7. 0 J
9. 27 J

5.3, pp. 82–83

4. energy, conserved, universe, lost, created, disappear, changed, form
5. acorn in tree: $E_m = 0.98$ kJ, $E_g = 0.98$ kJ, $E_k = 0$ kJ
   acorn 2.5 m above ground:
   Box 2: $E_m = 0.98$ kJ, $E_g = 0.49$ kJ, $E_k = 0.49$ kJ
   acorn on ground: $E_m = 0.98$ kJ, $E_g = 0$ kJ, $E_k = 0.98$ kJ

5.4, pp. 84–85

2. 96 %

5.5, pp. 86–87

2. 300 W
5. James Watt, steam engine
7. 5.3×10^4 J
8. 0.400 kWh

Chapter 5 Questions, pp. 90–91

1. (a)
2. (c)
3. (a) F
   (b) T
4. 1.0×10^2 J
7. (a) photosynthesis
   (b) gasoline-powered vehicle
   (c) electric vehicle
   (d) hydroelectric power plant
   (e) bicycle

6.1, pp. 92–93

1. joule
2. kinetic energy, potential energy
3. kinetic energy
4. potential energy
7. Anders Celsius, 100 °C, 0 °C, Daniel Gabriel Fahrenheit, 212 °F, 32 °F

6.2, pp. 94–95

2. temperature
3. temperature

6.3, pp. 96–97

1. lead
2. water
4. (a) quantity of heat, J
   (b) mass, kg
   (c) specific heat capacity, J/kg·°C
   (d) temperature change, K
5. 4.1×10^5 J
8. thermal expansion
9. thermal contraction

6.4, pp. 98–100

1. (a) gas
   (b) solid
   (c) liquid
2. between (a) and (b): increases, increases
   between (b) and (c): increases, remains unchanged
   between (c) and (d): increases, increases
   between (d) and (e): increases, remains unchanged
6. (a)
7. melts, freezes
8. evaporates, condenses
10. 7.5×10^3 J

6.5, pp. 101–102

5. T
6. greater, lower

Chapter 6 Questions, pp. 106–107

1. (d)
2. (b)
3. (a) T
   (b) F
5. 1.9×10^5 J

7.1, pp. 108–109

5. protons
6. nucleons

7.2, pp. 110–111

1. (a) strong nuclear force
   (b) electrostatic force
   (c) nucleons
   (d) protons
5. $^{238}_{92}U \rightarrow\ ^{234}_{90}Th + ^4_2He$
6. $^{238}_{92}U \rightarrow\ ^{234}_{90}Th + ^4_2He$

7.3, pp. 112–113

2. 4.2 mg
3. 50

6. (a) 20 000 years
   (b) 10 000 years

7.4, pp. 114–115

2. 3.0×10^8 m/s
4. smaller, smaller
6. greater, mass defect, the speed of light squared
8. (a) control rods
   (b) primary loop
   (c) fuel bundles
   (d) secondary loop

7.5, pp. 116–118

4. stable
7. 2.22 MeV
8. (a) plasma current
   (b) plasma
   (c) transformer coil
   (d) toroidal field coil

Chapter 7 Questions, pp. 121–122

1. (a)
2. (b)
3. (a) T
   (b) F
4. $^A_Z X \rightarrow\ ^{A-4}_{Z-2}Y + ^4_2He$
5. (b) 3.44 MeV
10. (a) nuclear energy
    (b) thermal energy
    (c) mechanical energy
    (d) electrical energy
11. (a) energy
    (b) nuclear stability
    (c) new atoms

Unit 3 Questions, pp. 123–124

1. (b)
2. (d)
3. (a) F
   (b) T
4. 2.0×10^2 W

Unit 4

8.1, pp. 126–127

1. T
2. (a) vibration
   (b) wave
   (c) neither
4. (b)
5. F
7. (b) gas
8. solids
9. steel

8.2, pp. 128–129

4. (a) closer together
   (b) farther apart
5. (a) greater
   (b) less
6. compressions, rarefractions
7. air, liquids, solids
10. longitudinal, transverse

8.3, pp. 130–132

1. (a) T
   (b) F

2. 1
3. transverse, longitudinal
4. (a) amplitude
   (b) wave speed
6. 0.25
7. in phase
8. 1 Hz, 1 s
9. frequency, one cycle per second
10. F
11. time, multiply

8.4, pp. 133–134

6. (a) F
   (b) T
7. decreased, mass, length
8. increased

8.5, pp. 135–136

1. 20 000
2. infrasonic, below
5. 0.606 m/s
7. F
8. watts, square metre
11. 0 dB to 130 dB
12. (a) 20 dB
    (b) yes

8.6, p. 137

4. airflow, angled
6. speed of sound, sound, a sonic boom

Chapter 8 Questions, pp. 140–141

7. 0.4
9. 1.0×10^2 m/s
10. F
11. 2.6×10^2 Hz
12. Mt. Burgess: 310 m/s
    Lake Louise: 320 m/s
    Banff: 320 m/s

9.1, pp. 142–143

2. (b)
3. 1.5
4. (b)
5. (a)
6. destructive interference

9.2, pp. 144–146

1. transmitted, reflected
3. (a) fixed-end reflection
   (b) free-end reflection
7. standing wave
9. F
10. (b) $L = \dfrac{\lambda}{2}$
11. $\lambda_1 = 2L$, $\lambda_2 = L$, $\lambda_3 = \dfrac{2}{3}L$
13. 2, 4, 6
14. 0.94 m
15. 660 Hz

9.3, pp. 147–148

1. F
6. T

9.4, pp. 149–150
2. (a) back and forth
   (b) absorbs, friction, air resistance
   (c) stops

9.5, pp. 151–152
1. (a)
4. (a) 1.0×10^2 Hz
   (b) 99 Hz
5. less, greater, greater
6. zero, speed of sound
7. zero, undefined

Chapter 9 Questions, pp. 155–156
1. (a)
2. (a) F
   (b) F
4. (a) 0.750 m
   (b) No. (1.50 m)
5. (a) 72 cm, 36 cm, 24 cm
   (b) 4.5 Hz, 9.0 Hz, 14 Hz
6. 1.41 times
7. (a) 20.1 m/s

10.1, pp. 157–159
2. pressure, vibrations, electrical impulses
3. magnifies, 10
7. air, fluid
8. higher, inward, lower, particles, frequency
9. T
11. F

10.2, pp. 160–162
8. (a) 702 Hz
9. T
10. wavelength, frequency

10.3, pp. 163–164
5. echoes/reflections
6. one or two seconds
11. flat, concave, convex, disperse

10.4, pp. 165–166
4. (a)

10.6, p. 169
6. flutter, vibration, wings, amplitude, duration

10.7, pp. 170–171
5. reflect, 110
8. T
9. low, 15–35
10. F
11. T

Chapter 10 Questions, pp. 173–174
1. (d)
7. (a) 0.290 m

Unit 4 Questions, pp. 175–176
1. (b)
2. (a)
3. (a) F
   (b) T
7. mechanical resonance

8. (a) 2.0 m
   (b) 1.0 m
   (c) 36 N
9. first harmonic: 5.0×10^2 Hz
   second harmonic: 1500 Hz

Unit 5

11.1, pp. 178–180
1. no, lost
3. (c)
4. 8.0 W
5. 8100 J
6. (d)
7. (a) 1.0×10 kWh
   (b) 3.7×10^7 J
8. 0.30 kWh
10. 6.6 h

11.2, p. 181
1. compress, gas

11.3, pp. 182–184
2. (a)
3. T
4. (b)
6. 14 V
7. (b)
8. 450 C
10. (a) A
    (b) C
    (c) B
    (d) electrons closest together: A
        electrons farthest apart: B

11.4, p. 185
1. (a)
2. positive

11.5, pp. 186–187
1. electrons, negative, positive
3. (a)
4. F
5. in series
6. 16 C
7. 25 μA
9. T
10. 75 min

11.6, pp. 188–190
1. T
2. (c)
3. (b)
4. (a) $I_{series} = I_1 = I_2 = I_3$,
       $I_{parallel} = I_1 + I_2 + I_3$
   (b) $V_{series} = V_1 + V_2 + V_3$,
       $V_{parallel} = V_1 = V_2 = V_3$
5. (a) 12 V
   (c) 4.0 V
6. (a) 0.60 A
   (c) I_1
   (d) 0.35 A
   (e) 0.35 A
   (f) 0.60 A
7. (a) 30.0 V
   (b) 10.0 V
   (c) 0.100 A
   (d) 0.300 A

11.7, pp. 191–192
1. high
2. F
3. (b)
4. (a)
5. F
6. ohmmeter, parallel
7. 96 Ω
10. (a) (iii)
    (b) (i)

11.8, pp. 193–195
1. current
2. decrease
3. T
4. F
5. (a) $I_{series}R_{series} = I_1R_1 + I_2R_2 + I_3R_3$
   (b) $R_{series} = R_1 + R_2 + R_3$
   (c) 14 Ω
6. (b)
7. (d)
8. (a) 29.0 Ω
   (b) 5.46 Ω

11.9, pp. 196–199
1. (a) 4.0 Ω
   (c) 13 V
   (d) 0.3 A
2. (a) 7.194 Ω
   (b) 0.6000 A
   (c) $V_1 = 6.000$ V
       $V_4 = 19.68$ V
   (d) 4.320 V
   (e) $V_2 = V_3 = 4.320$ V
   (f) 0.36 A
3. (b) 30.00 V
   (e) 14 Ω

Chapter 11 Questions, pp. 201–202
1. energy
2. potential, volts
3. gasification
4. series, parallel
5. positive
6. (b)
7. 130 W
8. 24 V
9. 1 h 23 min
10. (a) 15 V
    (b) 15 V
    (c) B and C
11. 12 Ω
12. (a) 3.75 Ω
    (b) 16.00 Ω
    (c) 1.25 A

12.1, pp. 203–205
1. T
2. north
3. south, north
4. (d)
6. F
8. (a)
10. (b) (ii)
    (c) (i)

12.2, pp. 206–208
1. reversed
2. perpendicular
12. (b)

12.3, p. 209
3. (c)

12.4, pp. 210–212
1. parallel
2. (b)
6. (c)

12.5, pp. 213–215
1. (b)
2. electric motor
4. repulsive, attractive
5. (b) same direction
   (c) different directions

12.6, pp. 216–218
1. single, continuous
2. rotor, sensor
4. T
8. several splits

12.7, p. 219
1. F
4. (a)

Chapter 12 Questions, pp. 221–222
1. (b)
2. (b)
5. (b) clockwise at point A
       counterclockwise at point B
8. (b) clockwise

13.1, pp. 223–224
1. magnetic field, electric current
2. F
3. (a)
5. (d)
6. F

13.2, pp. 225–226
1. opposes
2. F
3. (a) repelling force
   (b) south pole
4. (a) attractive force
   (b) north pole
6. (b), (e), (a), (c), (f), (d)

13.3, pp. 227–228
1. alternating
2. T
4. energy
5. (b)
6. F
7. (c)
9. (b)
10. (a) red and white, or black and white
    (b) red and black
11. (a) 120 V

13.4, pp. 229–231
1. external
2. T
3. slip rings

4. (c)
7. (b) slip ring 2
   (c) right side
   (d) positive
10. (a) north pole
    (b) right-hand rule for coils

13.5, pp. 232–234
1. step-down, decrease
2. (d)
3. (a) increases
4. (a) step-down transformer
   (b) step-up transformer

(c) greater than 20 V
(d) (i)
(e) 0 V
5. (a) $\dfrac{V_p}{V_s} = \dfrac{I_s}{I_p}$

   (b) $\dfrac{I_s}{I_p} = \dfrac{N_p}{N_s}$
6. 43 V
8. (a) 12
   (b) 0.0027 A

13.6, pp. 235–236
1. alternating, direct
2. T
3. high, low
5. (b)
7. (a) 25 kW
   (b) 83 %

Chapter 13 Questions, pp. 238–239
1. change
2. (b)

6. (a) 20
   (b) 0.050 A
7. increase

Unit 5 Questions, pp. 240–241
1. (d)
2. potential energy
3. 81.8 V
4. 1 h 56 min 40 s
5. 1.6 A
8. 350 windings, 0.43 A
9. 6.09 %

Appendix

A-1 Taking Notes: Identifying the Main Ideas

- *Identify and highlight the main ideas.* Main ideas are key concepts within a text. Text features such as headings, subheadings, boldfaced or italicized words, and graphic clues help to identify the main ideas in a text.
- *Identify and underline the details.* Details clarify or elaborate on the main ideas within a text.
- When you study for an exam, focus on the main ideas, not the details.

EXAMPLE

Pure Substances

All matter can be classified as pure substances or mixtures. A **pure substance** is matter that contains only one type of particle. For example, copper wire is made from only copper particles. Water is a pure substance that contains only water particles. A **mixture** contains two or more pure substances, such as table salt dissolved in water, or iron mixed with sulfur.

Pure substances can be further classified as elements or compounds. Elements are the basic building blocks of matter. An **element** is a pure substance that cannot be changed into anything simpler. An element contains only one kind of particle. By 1000 BCE, the physical properties of some of the metal elements (such as copper, zinc, silver, and gold) were understood, but none of these were recognized yet as elements. Today, we know that there are at least 116 elements.

Description/Discussion of Strategies

Read the sample text above and note the text features. Remember that text features such as headings and boldfaced words signal key concepts. Notice that the above text has the heading "Pure Substances." The heading is a text feature that tells you the topic of the text. It gives you important information and is, therefore, a key concept. Highlight the heading. Now look at the boldfaced words in the text: **pure substances**, **mixture**, and **element**. Boldfaced words identify vocabulary terms. Here, the boldfaced words are embedded in vocabulary definitions and tell you what the words mean. Highlight vocabulary definitions as they are key concepts, too. Finally, take a look at the opening sentences in both paragraphs of the above text. The opening sentences give you a quick overview of the information in the two paragraphs and should also be highlighted as key concepts.

Now that you have identified the main ideas in the above text, try to find the details. Look for sentences that add to the main ideas you identified above. The sentence "For example, copper wire is made from only copper particles" is an illustration of the sentence "A **pure substance** is matter that contains only one type of particle." It is a detail and should be underlined. Similarly, the last three sentences in the text are also details because they tell more about elements, the main idea. Underline the three sentences.

PRACTICE

Read the following text and complete the activities below.

Types of Electric Charge

A **static charge** is an electric charge at rest. The charge that you acquire as you walk across a carpet is called a static charge because it stays on you until you touch a metal doorknob. When you touch the doorknob, the charge moves from you to the door. Although some objects may keep a static charge for some time, eventually the static charge is **discharged**, or lost, to other objects in the air. Static charges tend to last longer indoors on winter days when the heated air is very dry. The study of static electric charge is called **electrostatics**.

1. Highlight the main ideas in the text.
2. Underline the details in the text.

Now read the following text and answer the questions that follow.

Some materials, such as acetate and vinyl, are able to acquire electric charges that stay on them for some time. These materials are called insulators. An **insulator** is a substance in which the electrons are so tightly bound to the atoms making up the material that they are not free to move to a neighbouring atom. Plastic is a good insulator. It is used to coat wires and extension cords to protect us from electric shock.

Other materials, such as aluminum and copper, are called conductors. A **conductor** allows electrons to flow freely from one atom to another. Metals are good conductors. Some materials, such as carbon, silicon, and germanium, are semiconductors because they allow electrons to move although there is some resistance.

1. Which sentence from the text does *not* contain a main idea?
   (a) An insulator is a substance in which the electrons are so tightly bound to the atoms making up the material that they are not free to move to a neighbouring atom.
   (b) Plastic is a good insulator.
   (c) It is used to coat wires and extension cords to protect us from electric shock.
   (d) A conductor allows electrons to flow freely from one atom to another.
2. Explain the difference between a main idea and a detail.

A-1 Taking Notes: Reading Strategies

The skills and strategies that you use to help you read depend on the type of material you are reading. Reading a science book is different from reading a novel. When you are reading a science book, you are reading for information.

BEFORE READING

Skim the section you are going to read. Look at the illustrations, headings, and subheadings.

- *Preview.* What is this section about? How is it organized?
- *Make connections.* What do I already know about the topic? How is it connected to other topics I already know about?

- *Predict.* What information will I find in this section? Which parts provide the most information?
- *Set a purpose.* What questions do I have about the topic?

DURING READING

Pause and think as you read. Spend time on the photographs, illustrations, tables, and graphs, as well as on the words.

- *Check your understanding.* What are the main ideas in this section? How would I state them in my own words? What questions do I still have? Should I reread? Do I need to read more slowly, or can I read more quickly?
- *Determine the meanings of key science terms.* Can I figure out the meanings of terms from context clues in the words or illustrations? Do I understand the definitions in bold type? Is there something about the structure of a new term that will help me remember its meaning? Which terms should I look up in the glossary?
- *Make inferences.* What conclusions can I make from what I am reading? Can I make any conclusions by "reading between the lines"?
- *Visualize.* What mental pictures can I make to help me understand and remember what I am reading? Should I make a sketch?
- *Make connections.* How is the information in this section like information I already know?
- *Interpret visuals and graphics.* What additional information can I get from the photographs, illustrations, tables, or graphs?

AFTER READING

Many of the strategies you use during reading can also be used after reading. For example, your textbook provides summaries and questions at the ends of sections. These questions will help you check your understanding and make connections to information you have just read or to other parts in the textbook.

At the end of each chapter are summary questions and a vocabulary list, followed by a Chapter Self-Quiz and Chapter Review.

- *Locate needed information.* Where can I find the information I need to answer the questions? Under what heading might I find the information? What terms in bold type should I look for? What details do I need to include in my answers?
- *Synthesize.* How can I organize the information? What graphic organizer could I use? What headings or categories could I use?
- *React.* What are my opinions about this information? How does it, or might it, affect my life or my community? Do other students agree with my reactions? Why or why not?

- *Evaluate information.* What do I know now that I did not know before? Have any of my ideas changed because of what I have read? What questions do I still have?

A-1 Taking Notes: Graphic Organizers

Graphic organizers are diagrams that are used to organize and display ideas visually. Graphic organizers are especially useful in science and technology studies when you are trying to connect together different concepts, ideas, and data. Different organizers have different purposes. They can be used to

- show processes
- organize ideas and thinking
- compare and contrast
- show properties of characteristics
- review words and terms
- collaborate and share ideas

TO SHOW PROCESSES

Graphic organizers can show the stages in a process (**Figure 1**).

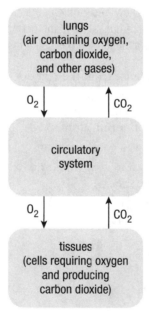

Figure 1 This graphic organizer shows that oxygen and carbon dioxide are transported around the body.

TO ORGANIZE IDEAS AND THINKING

A **concept map** is a diagram showing the relationships between ideas (**Figure 2**). Words or pictures representing ideas are connected by arrows and words or expressions that explain the connections. You can use a concept map to brainstorm what you already know, to map your thinking, or to summarize what you have learned.

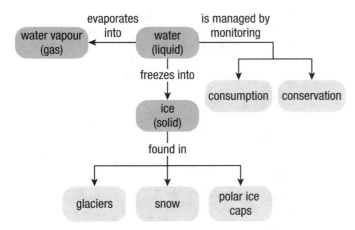

Figure 2 Concept maps show the relationships among ideas.

Mind maps are similar to concept maps, but they do not have explanations for the connections between ideas.

You can use a **tree diagram** to show concepts that can be broken down into smaller categories (**Figure 3**).

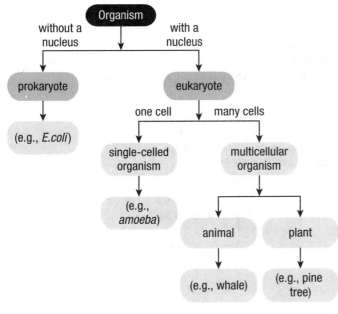

Figure 3 Tree diagrams are very useful for classification.

You can use a **fishbone diagram** to organize the important ideas under the major concepts of a topic that you are studying (**Figure 4**).

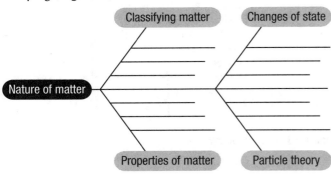

Figure 4 A fishbone diagram

You can use a **K-W-L** chart to write down what you know (K), what you want (W) to find out, and, afterwards, what you have learned (L) (**Figure 5**).

K	W	L
What I know	What I want to know	What I have learned

Figure 5 A K-W-L chart

TO COMPARE AND CONTRAST

You can use a **comparison matrix** (a type of table) to compare related concepts (**Table 1**).

Table 1 Subatomic Particles

	Proton	Neutron	Electron
electrical charge	positive	neutral	negative
symbol	p^+	n^0	e^-
location	nucleus	nucleus	orbit around the nucleus

You can use a **Venn diagram** to show similarities and differences (**Figure 6**).

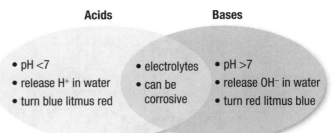

Figure 6 A Venn diagram

You can use a **compare-and-contrast chart** to show similarities and differences between two substances, actions, ideas, and so on (**Figure 7**).

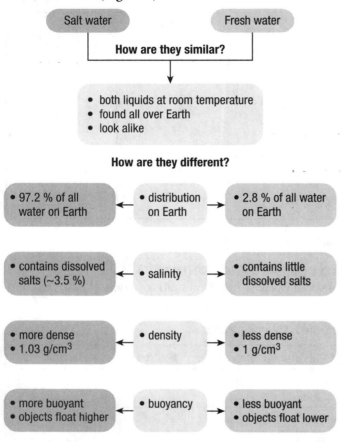

Figure 7 A compare-and-contrast chart

TO SHOW PROPERTIES OR CHARACTERISTICS

You can use a **bubble map** to show properties or characteristics (**Figure 8**).

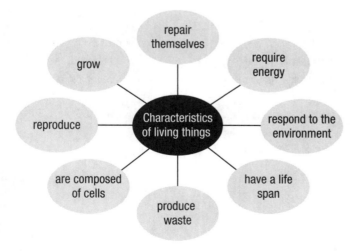

Figure 8 A bubble map

TO REVIEW WORDS AND TERMS

You use a **word wall** to list, in no particular order, the key words and concepts for a topic (**Figure 9**).

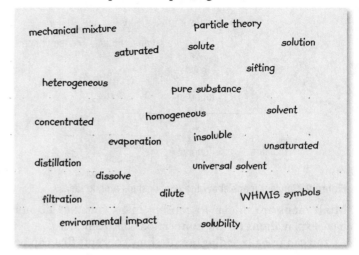

Figure 9 A word wall

TO COLLABORATE AND SHARE IDEAS

When you are working in a small group, you can use a **placemat organizer** to write down what you know about a certain topic. Then all group members discuss their answers and write in the middle section what you have in common (**Figure 10**).

Before:

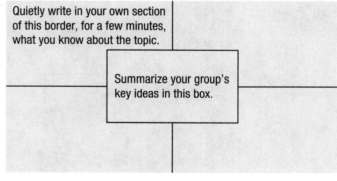

After:

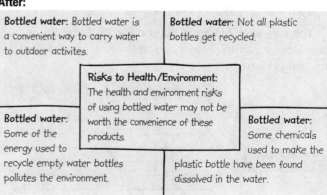

Figure 10 A placemat organizer

A-2 Answering Questions: Multiple-Choice Questions

- Read the question stem and attempt to answer it before looking at the answer choices.
- Analyze the key words or phrases that tell you what the question stem is asking.
- Read all the answer choices and choose one that most closely matches your answer.
- If your answer is not among the answer choices, reread the question stem. Sometimes slowing your reading pace can help you better understand the meaning of the question.
- Cross out any answer choices that you know are incorrect.

EXAMPLE

Read the following question stem:

Which layer of the Sun is outward from the convective zone and is also not a solid surface?

Description/Discussion of Strategies

Try to answer the question first without looking at the answer options (cover the options with a sheet of paper or with your hand). Then, look at the answer options below. Check your answer against the four choices given. Is your answer among the options? If yes, you have correctly answered the question.

(a) corona

(b) photosphere

(c) radiative zone

(d) solar prominences

If your answer does not match one of the options, use the next strategy. Note the key words in italics in the sample question. The key words and phrases are the essence of the question. They tell you what the question is expecting you to know or do. This sample question asks you to recognize a "layer" of the Sun that is "outward from the convective zone."

Look at the answer options. Which of them is a layer of the Sun? Are there any answer options that you know are wrong? You probably know that the corona and the radiative zone are not *outward from the convective zone*, so you can eliminate answer choices (a) and (c).

You have narrowed your possible answers to B and D, which are both outward from the convective zone. However, are these two *layers* of the Sun? Solar prominences are part of the photosphere, but they are not a layer of the Sun. Therefore, you can eliminate answer choice (d). You are left with option (b), which is the correct answer.

Complete the following multiple-choice questions using the tips you just read.

1. Which material is an insulator?

   (a) glass

   (b) copper

   (c) mercury

   (d) selenium

   Explain how you arrived at the answer to the above question.

2. Which of the following is a region of space surrounding an object that causes another object to experience a force?

   (a) vector

   (b) field

   (c) moment

   (d) range

   Were there any key words or phrases within the stem that identified what the question is expecting you to know? Explain.

3. Which of the following devices most likely uses alternating current?

   (a) a computer

   (b) a calculator

   (c) a light bulb in your home

   (d) an LCD television

   Which answer choices were you able to eliminate and why?

A-2 Answering Questions: Short-Answer/Written-Response Questions

A **short-answer question** is an open-ended question that requires a response. The question could ask for a definition, an explanation, or an example. It could also be a calculation or a completion activity. Depending on the type of short-answer question, the response will vary in length from a single sentence to a few sentences.

- Read the question carefully to understand the type of response required.
- Organize your response before writing it by making an outline, listing main points, drawing a sketch, or creating a graphic organizer.
- Make sure you answer all parts of the question. Eliminate any unnecessary information from your answer so it is clear and concise.

Read the following selection and answer the short-answer question:

The Phases of the Moon

During the new moon phase, the Moon is not visible from Earth (except during a solar eclipse). We do not see the new moon because the side that is illuminated by the Sun is not facing us. After this phase, the positions of Earth and the Moon allow a larger and larger portion of the Moon's illuminated side to be seen from Earth. The Moon is waxing, or appearing to increase in size. The waxing crescent Moon appears like an arched sliver of light.

1. Describe two phases of the lunar cycle.

Description/Discussion of Strategies

Read the question and identify what type of short-answer question it is. This sample question asks you to *describe* two phases of the lunar cycle. In other words, the question requires an answer that is at least a couple of sentences long. Notice that five lines have been provided for you to write your answer. Use this to estimate your answer's length.

Start by writing down the main points that your answer should cover. These notes will help you craft a complete answer. The sample notes below list the main points regarding two phases of the lunar cycle.

SAMPLE STUDENT NOTES:

– *new moon phase is usually not seen from Earth*

– *new moon phase is seen during a solar eclipse*

– *illumination increases after new moon phase*

– *waxing crescent is a curved slice of light*

You will build your answer from these bullet points. After writing an answer, read it to make sure you have answered the question correctly and completely.

Finally, eliminate any information in your answer that is unnecessary or that does not pertain to the question. If your response is very long, condense the information to make it brief and succinct.

SAMPLE ANSWER:

Two phases of the lunar cycle are the new moon phase and the waxing crescent. The new moon phase is usually not seen from Earth because the side of the Moon that faces us is not illuminated. The new moon phase can be seen only during a solar eclipse. Illumination of the Moon increases after the new moon phase. During the waxing crescent phase, the Moon looks like a curved slice of light.

Complete the following short-answer questions, using the selections below and the tips you just read.

Nuclear Fusion

A particular type of nuclear reaction powers the stars, and knowledge of these reactions can help us understand how stellar objects are formed and how they die. These reactions can also potentially provide society with a clean, renewable source of power. Unlike fossil fuel reactors, nuclear fission reactors are very clean in that they emit very small quantities of pollutants into the atmosphere. However, fission reactors have some negative environmental effect. The radioactive waste products are potentially harmful if not disposed of properly. This has led scientists to seek a cleaner source of power in the form of nuclear fusion. Nuclear fusion is a nuclear reaction in which the nuclei of two atoms fuse to form another element. Nuclear fusion is the opposite process of nuclear fission.

1. What are one advantage and one disadvantage of nuclear fission reactors?

The Difference Between Mass and Weight

The terms "mass" and "weight" are used interchangeably in everyday language, but these two words have different meanings. Mass it the quantity of matter in an object. The only way to change the mass of an object is to either add or remove matter. The mass of an object does not change due to location or changes in gravitational field strength. The units of mass are kilograms, and mass is measured using a balance.

Weight is a measure of the force of gravity acting on an object. Since weight and the force of gravity are the same quantity, the weight of an object depends on location and the magnitude of Earth's gravitational field strength at that location. Weight is a vector, and its magnitude is measured in newtons with a spring scale or a force sensor.

2. What is the difference between mass and weight?

Characteristics of Musical Sounds

Musical sounds have three main characteristics: loudness, pitch, and quality. These characteristics are subjective because they depend not only on the source but on the perception of the listener. The loudness a person hears depends on both the ear hearing the sound and the source of the sound.

The pitch of a sound is related to the frequency of the sound waves. The pitch detected by a person depends on the observer, the complexity of the sound, and even the loudness.

A tuning fork makes a simple musical note consisting of one frequency, but most musical instruments produce music composed of a fundamental frequency as well as several harmonics. The quality of a musical sound is the pleasantness of the sound. Sound quality depends on the number of harmonics, besides the fundamental frequency, and the intensity of these harmonics.

3. Describe the characteristics of musical sounds.

A-3 Solving Numerical Problems Using the GRASS Method

In physics, you sometimes have problems that involve quantities, units, and mathematical equations. The GRASS method is an effective method for solving these problems. This method always involves five steps: Given, Required, Analysis, Solution, and Statement.

SAMPLE PROBLEM

What is the gravitational potential energy of a 48 kg student at the top of a 110 m high drop tower ride relative to the ground?

Given: $m = 48$ kg; $h = 110$ m; $g = 9.8$ N/kg ◀——— Read the problem carefully and list all the values that are given. Remember to include units.

Required: E_g, gravitational potential energy ◀——— Read the problem again and identify the value that the question is asking you to determine.

Analysis: $E_g = mgh$ ◀——— Read the problem again and think about the relationship between the given values and the required value. There may be a mathematical equation you could use to calculate the required value using the given values. If so, write the equation down in this step. Sometimes it helps to sketch a diagram of the problem.

Solution: $E_g = mgh$ ◀——— Use the equation you identified in the "Analysis" step to solve the problem. Usually, you substitute the given values into the equation and calculate the required value. Do not forget to include units and to round your answer to an appropriate number of significant digits. (See Skills Handbook Sections X.X and X.X in your textbook.)

$$= (48 \text{ kg})\left(9.8\ \frac{\text{N}}{\text{kg}}\right)(110 \text{ m})$$

$$= 5174 \text{ N} \cdot \text{m}$$

$$E_g = 5.2 \times 10^4 \text{ J or } 52 \text{ kJ}$$

Statement: The student has 52 kJ of gravitational potential energy at the top of the ride relative to the ground. ◀——— Write a sentence that describes your answer to the question that you identified in the "Required" step.

PRACTICE

Solve the following problems using the GRASS method.

1. How much heat is needed to raise the temperature of 2.2 kg of water from 20 °C to the boiling point? T/I

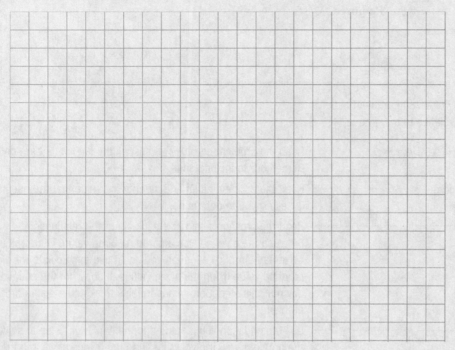

2. The wavelength of a water wave in a ripple tank is 0.80 m. If the frequency of the wave is 2.5 Hz, what is the wave's speed? T/I